National Writers Series

Writers Series of Traverse City

2022 LITERARY JOURNAL

A Year-Round Book Festival

Copyright ©2022

Published by National Writers Series
PO Box 5833
Traverse City, MI 49696
All rights reserved.
ISBN: 978-1-958363-03-4

Printed in the United States of America
Cover Design: Jacque Burke
Editors: Besty Moore, Ella Smith, and Jacque Burke
Book Production: Mission Point Press
www.missionpointpress.com

For additional copies, please visit
https://nationalwritersseries.org/raising-writers/

CONTENTS

NWS Creative Writing Lab

Creative Writing Workshops

North Ed Writers Studio at Career Tech

POETRY

FICTION

PLAYS

Introduction — Raising Writers

The National Writers Series (NWS) is a nonprofit organization dedicated to engaging world-renowned authors in meaningful conversations in the Traverse City area. Our goal is to understand better issues and ways of life within and outside our rural boundaries. We are also "Raising Writers" with programs that help students express themselves, explore the world through reading, develop their imaginations, and think critically.

Each year, NWS showcases the work of our Raising Writers programs in the *National Writers Series Literary Journal*, including poems, stories, plays, and literary nonfiction pieces.

This year the *National Writers Series Literary Journal* opens with the work of Traverse-area students who submitted winning pieces and honorable mentions for our College Scholarship Competition, held in partnership with the Grand Traverse Regional Community Foundation. Since 2010, NWS has awarded $60,000 including these most recent awards.

Next, you'll find stories and poetry written by students enrolled in the Front Street Writers Creative Writing Lab, an online creative writing program for highly motivated middle and high school students who are passionate about the craft of writing.

Students' stories, poems, and plays from the North Ed Writers Studio at Career Tech are also included. The Writers Studio is a North Ed Career Tech program that offers a creative home and college credit for eleventh- and twelfth-grade high school students. NWS provides North Ed Writers Studio students with masterclasses taught by visiting authors, opportunities to publish in the literary journal, and paid internships with our staff.

NWS also partners with Northwestern Michigan College, which offers creative writing classes through College for Kids for students elementary to high school age. We help recruit instructors and market these classes, knowing how important it is to sustain summer writing classes for youth. When College for Kids isn't in session, NWS hosts a variety of virtual writing workshops for students throughout northern Michigan. Though not featured in this year's journal, we must acknowledge the young poets we support at two area elementary schools. Fourth and fifth graders from Blair and Traverse Heights elementary schools enroll each year in NWS Poetry Workshops and produce a publication of their own. Held over several weeks, the workshops were taught by the wonderful Sam Collier, a poet and playwright. These students wrote poems that touched our hearts, and if you are interested in their work or volunteering to assist these young poets, please get in touch with education@nwstc.org.

NWS is dedicated to building the skills of our future storytellers. Our educational efforts focus on giving students a place to dream and believe while providing a safe space and freedom to express themselves in an unabashedly creative way. We nurture young readers and writers' inquisitive and imaginative minds, encourage them to ask "what if," and then help them bring the answer to these questions to life. Writing is magic. With pen to paper or fingers to keyboard, one can create an entire universe. One can live vicariously through the written word and have unimaginable adventures. Bringing stories to life through writing and reading is true magic. We at NWS hope that young people who participate in our programs will develop a lifelong love of reading and writing. We look forward to the day when we get to invite a Raising Writers alumnus to the Opera House stage!

If you are interested in supporting our education programs, please contact NWS Education Manager Jacque Burke at education@nwstc.org. You can find more information at nationalwritersseries.org.

Thank you for reading and supporting our young writers and readers!

—The National Writers Series Staff and Board of Directors

Acknowledgments

We are deeply grateful to all those who have supported the Raising Writers program; we couldn't do it without you! NWS's Raising Writers programs are made possible by private donations, sponsors, and grants from the Michigan Arts and Culture Council for Arts, Oleson Foundation, and the National Endowment for the Arts.

The *National Writers Series Literary Journal* is a team effort. Our thanks go to Mission Point Press; Front Street Writers: Creative Writing Lab Instructor Kevin Fitton; North Ed Writers Studio instructor Teresa Scollon and intern Ella Smith; and Betsy Moore for volunteering her time and energy to proofread this remarkable volume.

And, of course, thanks to all the young writers who worked so hard on their entries and dared to share them with the public. Thanks all!

NWS 2022
SCHOLARSHIP
WINNERS AND
HONORABLE
MENTIONS

THE RIVER

By Margaret Worden
Interlochen Arts Academy, 12th Grade

Once upon a time, there was a forest lush with life. The trees grew tall and beautiful, and the animals within hungered for nothing. The humans living in the town just outside of the forest spent much of their free time wandering within, hiking the trails, and picnicking in the green meadows. Children played hide and seek in the bushes, and old ladies picked wild raspberries to make into jam. It was a wonderful place to be, and it was so very loved.

However, the forest itself could not take credit for these achievements. Within the forest, there was a river, and it was this river that was the center of everything. The river was very old, older than both the town and the forest, so old that no one knew where it came from, where it ended or where it began. This may seem

like a silly distinction to make, for who would ever bother to wonder where a river came from, but I promise you it is an important distinction. Anything old enough for no one to remember its origins is guaranteed to have some magic of its own, and this river was very magical indeed.

The river had seen many things over the years. It had seen wars, senseless slaughter. Its waters had turned red with grief; it'd witnessed fates worse than death and crimes worse than hatred. It had seen the very worst of what humanity had to offer. This made it love and cherish the good parts of humanity even more. It had seen everything there was to death, and so it chose to see the value of life. It cherished peace and understood its importance. The river's magic was life itself.

It had grown the forest to replace the battlefield, to take something horrible and make something good out of it. It created a place of harmony and balance, and when the humans came along with their town, it welcomed them too. The river's kindness was endless because it was filled with love for everything around it.

The river's magic was apparent to everyone in the town. Everyone had a story to share about its waters. Hikers took note of how, when they drank from the river, they seemed to be filled with new energy, and those who dared to swim in it during the hottest months of the year often found themselves cured of the ailments they possessed. Artists who sat on its banks and listened to its gurgle found themselves finding exactly the kind of inspiration they needed to create their next masterpiece. Everyone believed in the river's power, and so the river was able to protect every one of the humans it cared for.

Almost everyone, at the very least. There was one girl who did not believe in the river. This was not out of spite. She simply did not have enough hope in her heart to believe much in anything, let alone magic. She was filled with a terrible melancholy, you see, the most hollow of woes. Living had become terrifying to her, and she was so very tired. She had no more tears to shed, let alone laughter or smiles. So she did not believe in the water that grew flowers that never wilted; she did not believe in the water capable of healing madness. So she did not think anything of jumping off the old wooden bridge that crossed over the river, on one uncharacteristically dark night.

There was no one around to watch her fall, and the forest was silent but for her cries, and when she hit its waters at a terrifying speed, the river did not know what to do. It could not calm its churning waters fast enough to save her bones from breaking on its rocks, and it could not stop its current from pulling her under fast enough to avoid the air leaving her lungs. But the river was magic, and had healed worse injuries with far less effort, so it did not think much of it. Only, when it tried to seal her bones back together, and return air to her lungs, did it find that the magic didn't work. Because the girl did not believe in magic, and magic can only enter the hearts of those who open themselves up to it. To the river's horror, it could do nothing to stop her heartbeat from becoming quieter and quieter until it settled into silence. The river's waters calmed, then, out of fright, becoming as smooth as glass, and the girl's broken body sank to the bottom of the river bed. The river cried out to the universe, begging it to make an exception, to change its rules, to just this once show kindness to its creations, but the universe shook its head. There was nothing to be done. The dead cannot be raised once they have fallen. This is the truth that the universe gave the river. The river was no stranger to death. It had already seen so much, after all. It took a moment to wonder if this was just the way of the world, a part of nature, the way things worked.

Then the river remembered that truth is subjective, and in the forest of its own creation, the river made its own rules. It decided that just because magic wouldn't work on someone who didn't believe in it didn't mean that that same person couldn't acquire magic of their own. The universe, realizing what the river meant to do, cried stop! You do not have the power to achieve this! And the river sneered and said *Yes, I do.* The river gathered up all of the magic it had stored over the years, the magic it had used to grow the trees and wildflowers, to heal the injuries of those it cared for, to protect the world it cherished, and gave it all away to the girl. Pushed it all into her small, unmoving body, and let its magic become *her* magic. Some will tell you that there is no magic strong enough to raise the dead. Others know that there is, and it is called love.

The girl's bones did not only mend, they became unbreakable, and her lungs not only filled with air, but learned how to breathe where there wasn't any, and her heartbeat not only returned but it returned louder than ever before, a melody more full of life than anything. It was not the river's power that did this. It was her own, and the magic stayed with her even after she opened her eyes again, for it would stay with her for the rest of her life, and perhaps even beyond that. The girl climbed out of the river, as healthy as could be, and took a moment to look back at the still waters. She wondered why the forest seemed so quiet, so still. Like it was grieving something. Why the flowers along the riverbank seemed to be wilting when she had never seen so much as a spot on a leaf before. But something ancient told her that she should hurry home, something tender and soft nestling in her heart as she found that for the first time in a long time, she had hope for tomorrow. When the girl left the forest, she found that she was brave enough to live.

That night, a horrible storm raged through the forest. Thunder cracked and lightning flashed, the wind screamed as rain fell across the land one last time. When the townspeople woke up the next morning, they found that despite all of that rain, the riverbed was as dry as a desert, almost like the river itself had gotten up and walked away. The forest withered after that, the animals moved to new ground and the people packed up and left the town as they inexplicably found that what had drawn them to the area was now gone. The stories of the magic river faded with time, existing only in the memories of the earth and the whispers of the wind.

In the place where dead things that shouldn't have been able to die reside, the universe asked the river that no longer was, why it had made its choice. Why it had given all of its power away; why it had chosen to fail in its task to protect what it cared about, and the river smiled.

The river said, *I did not fail, the girl was someone worth protecting,* and the universe said, *all she'd ever done was exist,* and the river said *Yes, I know. Isn't it magnificent?* And what of the girl? The one filled with magic? Well, she went on to do wonderful things. She went on to be as amazing as the river. She went on to save many people through kindness and love, and the world was a much better place with her in it. None of that was because she was magic, however. It was because she was herself.

2022 Winner of the Community Foundation

Leslie Lee Nonfiction Scholarship Award

ROBERT FROST: SWINGING THE GOLDEN BRANCH

By Lauren May
Traverse City Central High School, 12th Grade

Escapism is a double-edged sword. In moderation, the practice of indulging fantasies of the past, present, or future provides solace. Yet if avoiding the truth doesn't galvanize one to take action, escapism only harms. Robert Frost addresses the fine line between coping and avoidance as a solution to the darkness permeating everyday life. A young boy who dies too soon; the war between Earth's love and Heaven's innocence; especially the cyclical beauty and desolation of nature: Robert Frost infuses life's darkness into his poems 'Out, Out-', "Birches," and "Nothing Gold Can Stay," respectively. In each poem, the truth is too difficult to take at face value. Thus, Frost suggests that we escape, within reason, from the things that haunt us — death, aging, and imperfection.

Brief and chaotic, human life is only a spark in the scheme of the universe. Paradoxically, every moment feels permanent. Monsters within and without can make an escape tantalizing...until that escape is unwanted and unending. Dying too soon, the young boy in 'Out, Out-' battles many monsters; child labor and a growling buzzsaw bring about his end. At the moment of contact, when the exhausting and precarious day is almost at an end, the buzzsaw "Leaped out of the boy's hand, or seemed to leap—." Just as humans tend to personify their demons, so Frost gives a violent intent to the boy's saw. The tool also epitomizes the danger and injustice of this young boy "Doing a man's work, though a child at heart—" and constantly in danger. This constant press of work makes this young boy value even the smallest pleasures — thirty minutes less of work would mean the world, providing a small escape from his physical and mental exhaustion. Yet, since he was not allowed to step away, he dies under "the dark of ether." Here Frost illustrates the importance of moderate escapism to prevent catastrophe. In 'Out, Out-', escape for the boy means rest, and, for his family, it means avoidance. At the end of the poem, his companions "returned to their affairs," which appears callous. Frost leaves the morality and impact of this decision in question, implicitly arguing that the family has a right to give themselves the space denied to the boy. Whether escape from darkness is physical or emotional, it can mean the difference between life and death.

Fantasies of an ideal world come from two sources: the past and the future. Putting a rosy tinge on past events or imagining a happier future, respectively, make each present moment more bearable. Meanwhile, a major tenet of mindfulness is "living in the moment" and taking responsibility for current circumstances. Thus, in Frost's advocating for escapism, he appears to run counter to major spiritual principles. Yet Frost's "Birches" — a poem whose structure exemplifies the trio of past, present, and future — suggests that traversing through time can actually lead to more fulfillment. In the first section, lines 1-20, the narrator lives in the present moment, observing birch trees after a winter storm. These trees quickly become an allegory for the passage of time, where swinging at the hands of a young boy represents a pendulum swinging between past and future. The narrator would "like to think some boy's been swinging them. / But swinging doesn't bend them down to stay / As ice-storms do." No one wants to live their life enclosed by an icy exterior, held back from warmth and connection. These birches seem to exist in an eternal winter, unable to move away from their rigid present until the ice cracks and "You'd think the inner dome of heaven had fallen." The motifs of Heaven and Earth pervade this poem; Heaven represents escape, albeit temporary, while Earth represents the harsh messiness of life. Arising later in the third section, the dualling draw of Heaven and Earth helps the narrator move out of the past and into the future.

The second section — lines 21-40 of the poem — addresses the past through the narrator's nostalgic remembrances of his own time swinging birches. Many adults consider the innocence of their youth their happiest time, before "Truth broke in" and the darkness of the world revealed itself. True to form, the narrator reminisces about his boyhood by continuing his imaginings of a hypothetical "swinger of birches." This young boy was forced to entertain himself, being too far from the city to participate in sports or urban life. Like the young worker in 'Out, Out-', the swinger becomes mature and introspective beyond his years. Weaving in and out of adulthood, intertwining playtime with imagination, "One by one [the swinger] subdued his father's trees / ...Until he took the stiffness out of them." The swinger's father represents the rigidity of adulthood, planting birch trees in an orderly manner, only for his son to grab on to life and fly free. If the birches are a place for mental escape into the past and future, it is significant that the narrator emphasizes the swinger's reticence to "launch out too soon / And so not carrying the tree away / Clear to the ground." After all, a boy must not fly into his adulthood too quickly or dwell in escapist dreams of the future too often — an echo of Frost's implicit warning throughout his poetry. As the narrator finishes his recollection, the young swinger finally reaches the end of his youth, just as he reaches the top of a birch tree. With no more height to gain, he lets time drag him down, "Kicking his way down through the air to the ground." Reality will always set in; time will always move on. The narrator moves forward out of his reverie but exemplifies the value of moderate, enjoyable escapism.

Finally, the narrator considers how he will address the future. Building upon the reminiscences of his innocent past and the alternating spread of time in the birches, the final lines 41-59 reintroduce the motifs of Heaven and Earth. When the smooth rhythm between past and future breaks through a cold, stagnant prison of ice, Frost describes the icy shards on the ground appearing as pieces of Heaven falling to Earth. Finding sustained escape and bringing some fragments of this experience back to earthly life is the narrator's ultimate desire. For the first time, the narrator exposes the messy and uncomfortable details of vacillating too often between past and future: "Life is too much like a pathless wood / Where your face burns and tickles with the cobwebs / Broken across it." One can lose their way in this journey, their vision clouded. Now, the narrator wishes to leave Earth and come back to start anew, the constant stress of life temporarily erased from his brain. Considering the former and current beauty of the birches as a way to remember the past, enjoy the present, and propel oneself into the future, the narrator sees that the birches, as an allegory not just for time but for the messiness of Earth, are "the right place for love." Humans walk a fragile line; escapism in nature ensures that one won't live to see it break.

Frost continues to offer a more macro perspective of nature

in "Nothing Gold Can Stay," reminiscing about the cyclical, fleeting nature of the world. As the narrator acknowledges in the final section of "Birches," Earth as a whole has such intense beauty that human life becomes overwhelming. Yet nature is instructive in how to accept the transience of life and beauty. Adding another dimension to his thematic purpose of moderate escapism, Frost laments the truth that "Nothing gold can stay." Why is escape enticing? It offers a respite from a world that feels impossible; escape can fortify our physical and mental reserves and lead to a better life. However, nature does not have this privilege. The seasons, ecological cycles, ever-changing interspecies relationships: all of these processes go on without deliberate respite. Meanwhile, everything necessary is accomplished; in lines 3-5, the photosynthesis of a tree turns a beautiful, delicate flower into a leaf, which eventually shrivels and falls to the ground, just like the boy leaping from great heights back to Earth. It is helpful to understand the cyclical patterns of nature as a mirror to human lives, providing a reminder that every micro failure or moment spent resting is inconsequential in the macro flow of time.

Minute details have become the primary focus throughout many aspects of modern life, appearing to improve productivity and focus while decreasing emotional introspection and child-like joy. Even as the matters of the world appear more pressing, it remains important to escape into one's head. Ideal versions of the past and future need not be burdens if, as Frost suggests, the inherent values of rest, youth, and nature pervade these speculations. The tragedy of human life is its abbreviated nature, but let the constant press of aging be a reminder to balance the darkness...if only with the light of a far-away Heaven.

RECORDING AND REMEMBERING

By Anna Sperry

Traverse City West Senior High School, 11th Grade

TRAVERSE CITY---John Brown and Noah Williams did not expect to become the talk of Traverse City when they launched a new element on the @tcwbleachercreatures Instagram account, interviewing students. They were just two seniors on the student Senate with an idea. They wanted to high-light TC West players with unique experiences on the field, as well as fans in the bleachers. Brown and Williams conduct on-the-spot interviews at games and at school. They share their work on their Instagram account, which continues to amass more followers (1,582 at the time of this article).

"I always try to interview the top finishers or [somebody that had] something extraordinary [happen] to them during their race," Willaims said.

Williams strictly covers cross country meets while Brown

covers soccer and football games. With students being allowed to attend games this year, Brown has encouraged students to take advantage of the opportunity to show up and support their peers. And students have done just that - show up to games with lots of school spirit.

"I was thinking about something that would kind of bring the energy up and awareness for the athletes and get more people to go to games," Brown said.

Most students attend the Patriot game but Brown hopes people will start going to other games. Several sports don't have a student section. Athletes like sophomore Ryan Davis want to see more students attending games and meets. Davis hopes Brown and Williams will continue to conduct interviews through all sports seasons to increase attendance and support of less attended sports like soccer, tennis and skiing. Davis is on the TC West ski team and hopes that someone will interview the skiers and post about their meets.

While they plan to feature athletes throughout all sports seasons, Williams would like to see the student Senate come up with something new every year that each class would be remembered for.

"If they want to keep [interviews] a tradition, that would be cool, but I also want to encourage [them] to figure out new, fun things for their [class]. The interviews, for us, work really well and may work really well for the next coming years but [student Senate should] keep coming up with new and interesting [projects]," Williams said.

Williams hopes future projects will involve the greater school community. In the meantime, posts focus primarily on varsity athletes, which means that younger players are less likely to be featured on the Instagram page if they don't make the varsity team.

"I think [it would] be really good to have other people [get] a chance to be interviewed who didn't this year because they're too young," Brown said.

Brown and Williams aren't limiting the interviews to just sports, they're expecting to expand them to other corners of the school community.

"We're planning to interview some of the actors after the musical," Brown said. Students are always eager to see more interviews pop up on their Instagram feed. Brown and Williams have favorite interviews with a specific backstory. Williams' favorite was from the second soccer game against Central.

"During the interview, they shut off all the lights and it was completely dark and [foggy]. I think that looked pretty cool," Williams said.

Almost all of the interviews involve the student section. Many students have been encouraged to come to games because of the possibility of being featured on the Instagram account. They feel excited when they see themselves highlighted on their feed.

"So far the Pink game [has been my favorite] because there [were] just a lot of [interviews] and everybody was super hyped up because it was a great game," Brown said. The only problem with the interviews is the fact that students really want to be seen on the Instagram page and sometimes the interviewers have to start over because of it. "A lot of people like to just barge into [the shot] in the middle of [the interview] so I have to keep rerecording," Williams said.

Overall, students love the interviews and don't have anything bad to say. Though, with anything, students have some preferences.

"The interviews with the student section are better than the interviews with the players. Everyone's just so hype," Davis said.

The interviewers don't look for anyone specific to interview, they just like to feature different types of people from the student section. Most of the time, Williams and Brown come up with the questions on the spot and the viewers really enjoy the informality of the interviews and the questions.

The interviews after games have become possibly one of the most loved and unique projects at school. Other schools in the Traverse City area have also enjoyed the interviews and have started conducting their own. Students at West are somewhat bothered by this and want to keep it an exclusively West tradition. They look forward to being interviewed and seeing their peers answer the light-hearted questions. Then again, imitation is the highest form of flattery. "We love John Brown," Davis said. Indeed.

HAPPINESS IS CRESTING

By Ella Rintala

Traverse City West Senior High School, 12th Grade

i — may

up through the blinds in the bathroom the moon is cold on its
    black paper
the pennsylvania water pricks my dry-picked oil-seeping skin and
    drums my tired bloat i'm a vinyl balloon inflated to capacity
i buzz as the air escapes
as i fizzle out i towel myself off different this time to keep it
    exciting
i make faces in the mirror through weeping stripes of wet my
    matte lips twisted a fragmented frown blurry and bored

i look now at the sliced up sky
and notice that the night is tumbling through the cracked
    window

the air is warm but its edges cut cooly
and the moon has started seeping
its beams are knotted around my neck's taut tendons crackling
    like dry roots at the stab of a shovel yet it means nothing
it's just a note taped to the wall in the hallway
a chill cresting
and happiness will crash with the white wave
        some people's faces remind me they have a hiding skull
    and their (my) skin smells like both dry leaves and leaving dry

when i dance in my room
i can't help but reincarnate a weightless shadow as a sleepy
    audience
i can't help but hope its belly glows and chest thumps at my
    familiar form and my purple joy together we watch the sun
    fade in ruby violets and blue blacks
the oxidized blood seeping into coffee stains seeping into
    seafoam into quiet blue
we joke that the clouds are so small and round it's like i poked
    circles out with a hole puncher so i could plie the sheets of the
    sky into my plastic binder
        but i can puff air into daydreams and only feel them
          if i want to like the socks clinging to my feet
        they make me feel nothing but bored desire to
          think about something else and maybe
          itchy i hope that my belly will glow soon
the girl who told me my aura was yellow told me that tonight
    there'd be a pink moon but it looks more blue

ii—june
mom and i saw two herons at the lake today. they were
thoughtfully placed on the shore like wooden sculptures around
a fountainous garden centerpiece.

the ripples on the lake fluttered like a book falling open,
shimmering like a powdery veil, like I'd feel its grainy
roughness if i scratched the surface, like it'd sting like static.
sitting on the slider, watching the family of loons lunge at fish,
i wanted to dive mouth-open into the water. i wanted the lake
to itch my tongue and throat, cool and heavy in my sandy lungs.
my favorite rock that arizona marie placed in my palm was
black and flat like a pupil, speckled with white fossils. like
stars through wet eyes. the downy dots on a loon's back,
migrating to cool lakes for the summer.

my ears are sore from sun squinting. my sternum
is sore from smiling so much.

FLOWERS KEEP FALLING (EXCERPT)

By Taryn Spencer
Kalkaska High School/North Ed Writers Studio, 12th Grade

Benjamin's stomach erupted out of his throat and into the glass porcelain bowl that stared back at him. A giant boulder sat on his chest as he gripped the cool, metal railing, trying to hoist himself up. This time though, the world decided that it wanted him on the floor and pulled the rug out from under his feet. The bright colors of something peculiar caught his eye.

The contents in the toilet bowl were not a grotesque mix of the various foods he had scarfed down for lunch, but instead a tiny garden. A plethora of flowers, covered in a thin layer of saliva, and... *is that blood?*

Suppressing the urge to lose his stomach again, Benjamin grabbed the railing with shaky hands and successfully pulled himself up. The world allowed it, even if he had to keep all his weight on that cool metal bar in order to stay upright. He hesitantly flushed the toilet, torn between obliterating any evidence of the flowers or crying for help for someone to validate that he was in fact throwing up roses. *It's no secret what throwing up flowers means.*

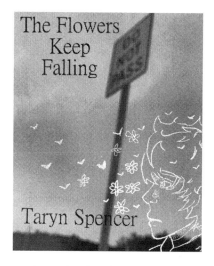

The Flowers Keep Falling

Taryn Spencer

A few years back, Benjamin sat in the living room of his cousin's house watching the television, when the sound of his aunt sobbing tore his attention away from *Jeopardy*. He ran into the kitchen and found Maria hunched over in pain; roses in the sink; blood on the floor. Between her hiccupping sobs he heard his aunt mutter something about "Maria being in love." and "How could something so beautiful be punished so harshly?"

It was true. The disease known as Hanahaki occurs when someone falls in unrequited love. Flowers begin to grow in their lungs, and the victim will cough up flowers until their feelings are either returned, or they suffocate from the petals. This could be avoided if the victim got surgery to remove the flowers, but the feeling of love would leave as well. Maria opted for surgery.

She was in love with a boy named Nick, who she never told. She waited, hoping that maybe he would miraculously return those feelings someday, but he never did. When her condition took a turn for the worse, she was brought to the hospital, and taken care of.

Nick had a different fate though. Months later, he showed up on the doorstep of the house with (ironically) flowers. He confessed his love for Maria and apologized for taking so long to realize it. She was unable to return his feelings because of the operation, and full of regret she sent him home. He opted not to have the surgery. Benjamin has prodded Maria a few times before out of curiosity, but she refuses to talk any more about it. Nick was Benjamin's age when he died.

Benjamin finally decided to flush the flowers, and they were gone just as abruptly as they appeared. He left the stall to find a completely ordinary, obviously not dying boy in the mirror staring back at him. His throat was scratchy, and he was definitely a little feverish– but he couldn't help but be grateful that no vines were growing out of his mouth and into his nostrils. *Life is just a series of simple positives.*

"Benjamin?"

The sudden noise made him jump, and he thought for a small moment, *maybe I actually am dying*, as his heart pounded in his ears against the sudden surprise. He whirled around to find bright orange hair and a smile looking up at him.

"Whoops." Eli laughed, "Didn't mean to scare you I– wow, you don't look very good. Are you alright?"

"Uh..." Benjamin tried to recompose himself, looking between Eli and the mirror. "I don't think I should go to rehearsal tonight."

"Yeah yeah, that's probably for the better," Eli said, "You look kind of awful... I can walk with you if you want."

I look awful... gee thanks, Eli. "I think I might just get a ride home from my mom. There's no reason for you to miss rehearsal too."

"That's probably for the better."

A weak, "Yeah," was all Benjamin could muster. A moment of silence stretched as Benjamin stood, clutching his stomach, unable to think of what he could say. He was glad that Eli was there despite the terrible conditions they were under. The thought of telling Eli about the flowers briefly crossed his mind but he thought better of it. *The idiot already isn't paying attention in class. I'm not worrying him with this. Besides, maybe I only imagined it, that happens sometimes when people get sick, right?*

Eli broke the silence first. "Hey listen... I can wait with you for your mom, just in case. Then I can tell the rest of the cast that you had to go home early because you were sick. I'm sure they'd understand. Well– all of them except for Amanda. You should probably text her."

"Right, her." Benjamin said, "You can wait with me if you want, only if you're okay with potentially getting sick."

"Of course, I don't mind," Eli said, holding the restroom door open. "It wouldn't be the first time you got me sick. I might miss school too, so hey, that's cool! It's probably just the stomach flu, it won't kill me."

It will kill me though.

They walked down the hallway with nothing but the sound of their footsteps, and a terrible itch that Benjamin could not scratch. Amanda was his girlfriend, but he didn't think that he loved her. He never felt the sparks or the moment of clarity that people mention when you first realize you've fallen in love. *If not Amanda, then... who?*

******

The wind that stroked Eli's face was refreshing. The sky was devoid of pigment, other than a thin slate blue, barely visible in the overpowering gray. This was his kind of morning. No rain to make his tennis shoes soggy and squish into his socks as he walked; no sun stinging his eyes and painting freckles on the back of his neck. Just the boy and his bike, blurring through a quiet town, holding a lunch to deliver to an ill friend. *If he even shows up today. I should have called.*

He slowed his pace as he felt his phone buzzing in his pocket. "Speak of the devil," Eli chuckled while pulling his phone out of his pocket. He answered quickly and wasted no time and asked, "Hey Benjamin, will you be at school today?"

"This is Amanda, actually. I was kind of wondering if you knew the same thing though. I know you said he wasn't feeling well but he hasn't responded to anything. I called him several times last night, but he declined them all."

I would have too, Eli thought, and then replaced the thought with a little bit of guilt. He thought Amanda was alright, just not for Benjamin. Something about her was... too perfect. "I haven't heard from him either. Must have been a bad flu I guess."

"I guess so, well thanks for the help anyway!" She said before he heard that familiar *click*.

Eli muttered to himself about the extra lunch. *I should have call-* he began to scold himself before he noticed a familiar stride walking on the side of the road. He pulled his bicycle up to Benjamin. The smell of roses filled his senses and he had to stifle a laugh. "Benjamin, are you wearing perfume?"

"Oh, hey Eli. No, I'm not. Shut up," Benjamin said. "I think my mom sprayed me on accident or something."

Eli giggled. "At least you smell good, for once. Here, take this." He held out the lunchbox he had been protecting with his life, and Benjamin took it. "It's for you. I knew you were sick, and I like to cook so... just be careful. Chicken noodle soup, an apple, and toast." "Were you careful on the bike?" Benjamin laughed.

"Uhhh... yes. Definitely."

"Mhmm." Behind his smile, there was a flicker of something else. Even if it was only for a brief moment, he could have sworn his friend was still in pain.

"So..." Eli asked, "Are you feeling better?"

"Honestly?"

"Of course, stupid."

Benjamin sighed. "I don't know. I practically begged my mom to let me stay in today."

"That seems kind of unlike her. Your mom is so sweet!"

"I know! I think... I think Amanda called her."

Amanda.

"Oh yeah... she called me this morning. She seemed pretty worried."

"I think I need to break up with her."

Eli stopped his bike. "Oh?"

"Oh." Benjamin mirrored his speech, sarcasm brimming on the edge of his voice but not quite spilling into it.

"I'm sorry dude."

"That's alright. I presume it will be a while before I can do anything about it but I like someone else."

Someone else?

"Who?" Eli asked.

Benjamin only laughed and kept walking, and Eli pedaled after him.

****

Benjamin felt a little bit better after he broke up with Amanda, which was a relief. He considered any easing of the pain in his lungs as an indication that he was doing something right. Feeling better did not equal feeling good enough to sit in class though. So he stared at the ceiling in the sickroom. The office had called his mom several times that morning, and she never picked up. Which was not unlike her. So, the school had no choice but to keep him there. They sighed every time they passed him, which made him feel bad. He realized that he would never allow the fact that he has Hanahaki to get out, ever. If just being in the sickroom deserved these sympathetic sighs, he didn't think he could handle it if everyone knew he was dying. Or in love.

By the time lunch rolled around, Benjamin had developed a plan. He didn't have to explain everything to Eli. He just had to find a way to get Eli to tell him who he was in love with- *That's... easy enough.*

He got signed out of the sickroom, telling the school nurse that he thought getting something to eat and a breath of fresh air might help. He snatched the lunch Eli made for him from his locker and rushed to their normal table in the far corner of the outside eating area.

Eli sat alone, the wind whipping his bright orange hair this way and that. Benjamin gripped the lunch box as he realized something he hadn't known before. He coughed up one single petal into his palm.

Eli?

ANGEL OF DEATH

By Madeline Henry

Traverse City West Senior High School, 12th Grade

Death.

It is ingrained from a young age to fear the end.

It is against societal odds if you are willing to welcome death.

Life does not come with an exact expiration date.

We live day after day, ignoring the fact death could always be around the corner.

My Grandmother Betty, passed away on Thanksgiving of 2020 from Alzheimer's. She was in a deep battle of fighting this disease, this angel of death.

As said by Lana Del Rey, "We were born to die."
The date is unpredictable.
You could die tomorrow or even in a year.
Everything happens in time.
Unpredictable time.

My family had seen her death almost as a blessing. It was extremely telling that the day she passed was a day specified for giving thanks. It was our time to remember and be grateful for the memories we shared with her. It was our time to give thanks to the person who she had been.
We are instructed to live every day to the fullest with death being certain. We take things day by day.
Against better judgment, we take things for granted.
We take life for granted.

I remember waking up at the cottage and seeing her on the porch on a sunny morning, drinking coffee at the picnic table. A straw in the mug because of the fear of staining her teeth. She would sit with her back to the cottage to watch the wind wrestle with the leaves on trees. Hummingbirds would zip by to get a taste of the sugary water she had put out the day before in the feeder.

Memories of going out for birthday dinners.
Sitting at campfires as the sun slowly drops below the horizon.
Bringing flowers to congratulate me after a long dance performance.
We take it all for granted.

My Grandmother drove me to dance class when my mom was out of town. She laughed with my Grandfather out on the pontoon as we jumped off into the glistening waters of Crystal Lake. And she would never allow her food to touch when she plated a meal.

It's these memories we keep close.
Memories with pure utter euphoria.
Memories with people in our inner circle.
It's what we cherished.
It was our lives.

My Grandmother was diagnosed with Alzheimer's in 2016. Although we had been devastated, we were not entirely surprised because Alzheimer's runs in the family. She was 71. To our dismay, time with our Grandmother had been cut short.

As the condition worsens, even when they aren't there, there is comfort in knowing they are still with you.
The fact they are living.
They still can be there when you need them.
It becomes difficult knowing you will lose someone.
That's what makes it painful.
You lose that comfort.

You realize the ugly truth will drag out in front of you, like a horrific car crash in slow motion that lasts for years. I felt I was becoming detached and withdrawn. It was then I started to wish death on my Grandmother. I loved her. I loved her with all my heart, but I wanted her dead to preserve the good memories. I didn't want them tainted with the dark ones. I wanted to preserve her heart. Keep the good memories in a small tight box with no room for error. My Grandma was a very proud and strong woman. Proud of her life, her children and grandchildren. She never wanted to be like this. She cried with us knowing all the things she would miss in life. She apologized for not being at future graduations and weddings.

Alzheimer's has the ability to destroy everything.
It takes away the reasons worth living.
Your memories.

Memories of the good times.
Only to be stripped of your values, character, and abilities.
You lose your soul.
It gets stolen from you.

The remembrance and comfort from your family gets stripped from your life. My Grandmother slowly forgot who I was, my brother, my cousins, and my mother. We were all erased from her memory. I would sit with her on the couch and reiterate what was for dinner, or as she had always called it, supper. She held my hand. The past two years, she had been living in fear of what was going on around her.

Nightmares are something that you can escape.
At some point your fear jolts you awake, drenched in sweat with a rapid heart beat. You made it; you escaped the horrific dream.

My grandmother's life quickly turned into a nightmare, only she couldn't escape. The delusions had started and brought waves of immense terror. Seeing things that weren't there. Communicating with people who were a pure figment of imagination. The struggle to differentiate between tv and movie characters being on a screen or alive in her living room.

Not knowing where you are.
Not knowing who you are with.
Let alone not knowing if you are safe.
Feeling completely alone.

Wanting to go home. Not knowing you are home.
It destroys you.

I remember the first time my Grandmother ran away from home.
My Grandfather had turned his back only for a minute to work on
dinner. And then click, the latch of the door closed. She ran until
she ran out of energy. My Grandmother was found an hour later
hiding in a stranger's garage. She was both terrified and screaming as if her life depended on it. We were family, but she had lost
all and any recognition of it.

And when you think things can't get worse.
You reach another level of rock bottom.
You question when rock bottom will truly be the bottom.

My Grandmother, who struggled to comprehend what was happening at moments, had lost the ability to understand basic human
functions. On a timed basis, my family and I would walk her to
the bathroom so she could relieve herself. We helped clean her.
We would help her undress and perform the necessary routine to
keep up with her wellbeing including feeding her.

Then another punch to the gut.
A slap on the wrist.
We made it to another level of rock bottom.

Although we had tried our best, the future was unpreventable. It
had become impossible for my family and Grandfather to take
care of her. Knowing regardless of what we did, we would never
be enough to help her, to take away the struggle. She needed to be
in a nursing home.

Retirement homes are where people go to die.
They have a way of tearing you down and making you feel nothing.

Frankly, my Grandmother had already lost everything. In movies, you often hear how people have nothing left to live for, but my Grandmother genuinely didn't. As if we were a whiteboard of her entire life, that had been wiped away. She could not talk, followed by the refusal to eat. She was now 90 lbs. She was making her deathbed without realizing it.

A zombie apocalypse had taken over.
Instead of a thirst for brains, it has a craving for memories and your livelihood.

My Grandma who I loved was gone. We were keeping a corpse alive, nothing but a breathing zombie. This is why I had wished death upon her to spare her any more suffering. It would save us from this pain; this heartache, for the Grandma I loved so much and had spent so many years with, was no longer. She hadn't been for quite some time. She was locked away in a nursing home for nearly a year with no ability to communicate.

Then your fear of what can happen finally happens.
Death.
You lose them.
All sense of comfort is lost.

I remember seeing her in the open casket, face with color, hair neatly placed. For the first time in years, she looked at peace. She was the woman I remember from my childhood; the one attempting to put my hair in a bun for dance; the one who loved the Grand Hotel's pecan balls on Mackinac Island.

I would be lying if I said I wasn't relieved. My Grandmother was no longer living in a horror movie, no longer suffering from delusions. I could rest easy knowing she finally was at peace.

I didn't cry over her death until roughly three months after. I sat in bed in the midst of a depression episode and pleaded with her ghost to tell me what to do. Only she didn't respond. The room was silent except for my sniffles. The comfort I had grown to know and love was gone. She wasn't there like she had been. Only silence and my tears.

I was 15 when she passed. I now sit in my fifth hour Environmental Science class, a senior in high school. I got my driver's license without her. I graduate at the start of June without her. I'm going to graduate without one of the most important people I would want to see at that moment. I hope to graduate from college in four years. I hope to get married in the next ten years. It will all be without her. My Grandmother is gone and there are never enough tears to bring her back.

OUT OF THE DARKNESS

*How the Traverse City Community
Approaches Addiction Treatment*

By Ted Arnold
Traverse City Central High, 11th Grade

Despite its dangers, addiction has long been a dinner-table taboo, a disease impossible to put into words. The process of recovery is a long and often hidden road, but not one that can be taken alone. Many services exist to help addicts recover and take important steps toward sobriety. Here in Traverse City, Addiction Treatment Services (ATS) has been providing assistance with recovery for over 40 years.

ATS offers a variety of services including a detox facility, residential services, and outpatient support. Dan Rockne, Access Manager at ATS, describes his job as "communication and coordination." Rockne is responsible for fielding calls from clients seeking help, as well as family members looking for ways to support their loved ones. Beyond that, he works internally to determine what kind of care someone will need. Rockne has access to a powerful tool when working with clients: he has personally felt the toll of addiction. For many drug and alcohol counselors, experience in recovery allows them to "look across as opposed to look down, it allows me to relate, and it's the most disarming thing that I can say to anyone." Rockne's first task is to "figure out: What are they using? How much are they using? Do they have other kinds of issues that are going on, as far as legal, social, medical?" Then, his team can figure out what it is going to take to treat them, and will they be safe to bring in?

Treatment varies depending on what substances someone is using, how frequently they're using them, and what sort of home environment someone is coming from. Rockne notes that having "people around you that are safe and supportive" is a very different recovery experience than "coming from a pretty chaotic environment," and as such, is something the team needs to factor in. As a result of this process, ATS can offer a full spectrum of care, allowing them to properly treat anyone who comes in.

According to Rockne, ATS uses their detox facility anytime that someone is using a substance and "develops a chemical dependence in their body." The facility is designed so that ATS can first assess and then provide constant care and observation to someone as they are medically withdrawn from those substances. This process is incredibly dangerous outside of supervision. Withdrawal from heroin is "like having the worst flu of your life for about 10 days," and someone with a dependence on alcohol will get a condition called the delirium tremens, when they are "liable to be hypertensive, be very ill, potentially have a seizure, [or] potentially die." The facility is "the best, most structured environment we can keep them in. They're under observation. If anything goes south and we don't have the capability to take care of it here, they're in the best position to go directly from our facility to the hospital." At the same time, some people will only have mild symptoms and will soon move to the next level of care.

After the detox program, ATS offers residential services at varying levels of supervision. The first level is highly supervised, where residents do a 30-day stay and have "intensive therapy with a designated therapist when they come in, and then they're also doing [some] kind of group work and developing those social interactions that they maybe didn't have or missed out on while they were using." A lower level is called recovery housing, which is a less structured environment where there is an expectation of maintaining sobriety, and of either employment or volunteer work. The benefit of this style is that "they're living a normal life where they come back at the end of the day and they stay in a sober environment." The lowest level is outpatient services, which "usually involves some sort of group component, and some sort of individual component [where] clients will go to our outpatient facilities."

For those who have fought addiction, like Patricia Steele, the idea that someone might see their struggle is "horrible and terribly embarrassing." Her family was very successful, but nearly everyone drank, and Steele was cursed by "the gene of alcoholism." As time went on, she slowly developed a dependency on alcohol. "My drinking increased and it went from once in a while on the weekends to regularly on the weekends, to once in a while during the week, to regularly during the week, all that kind of stuff." By the time she had reached her forties, she had experienced "a lot of ups and downs and my patterns of reaching for [alcohol] had increased. I was drinking it for all kinds of reasons." At that point "my second husband said to me 'I think you need to slow down on your drinking' and it wasn't until then that I realized I couldn't. So the more I tried, the more I found I couldn't, the more people wanted me to, the more I began to lie about it, the more I began to sneak alcohol, the more alcohol became an obsession for me, the more it started ruling my days."

Following a citation for driving under the influence of alcohol, Steele began to seek help.

Yet, after three trips to rehab, she still found herself coming back for a drink. In rehab she would "relax and let my guard down a little bit, I would feel comfortable with other people in the same circumstance. I would go to AA [Alcoholics Anonymous] with other people in the same circumstances and feel comfortable. But when I would go home, whether I was there for a month, or, in one place, three months, it was like the world expected me to be fixed." However, she wasn't fixed, and she found herself "not being able to talk about it, not being able to deal with it, not having the courage to say 'no, I still want a drink' or 'yes, I'm still drinking.'"

Then Steele's world flipped upside-down. On December 12, 2007, she got into an argument with a friend about her drinking. She left their house in anger. On her way home, she crossed the yellow line and hit another car head-on. The driver was killed, and the passenger was severely injured. Steele woke up days later in the hospital, having gone through several surgeries. Her first memory is of "my kids standing at the foot of my bed. I can remember the looks on their faces that were devastating." Two weeks later, she was taken to prison and later sentenced to seven years in jail. As a result, she was forced into sobriety. In prison, Steele was required to attend AA meetings, where she met a group of women who "seemed to see how broken I was and how much I hurt, how scared I was and all of those things. And they were the ones who finally taught me that I could let down my guard [and] I could be me." Steele's mentor in prison was "this wonderful grandmotherly type woman. She would say to me, 'Patty, if you could just put down your shame and your guilt just for a little while, you would have some room for healing, but you have to do that.'" After her release from prison, she devoted herself to becoming a drug and alcohol counselor, eventually landing at ATS, where she could use her experiences to help others with their struggle.

Recovery looks and feels different for everyone, and it's key to remember that addiction is "not just a black and white thing." Everyone struggles differently and recovers differently. Addiction is present everywhere, lurking just below the surface. Rockne thinks "we need to be sending the message of hope, and that if someone's breathing, they've got a chance, and that even as a young person, even high schoolers, they can get, and stay [sober] if they want to."

SELECTION FROM FATHERS: A COMPOSITION ON ACCEPTANCE

Thunderstorms

By Kianna Carpenter
Traverse City Central High, 12th Grade

How am I supposed to know what to do when the sound of your voice doesn't exist anymore? I thought I knew. Thought I was prepared. But suddenly, the "hey, buckeroo!" booming from the phone will be gone. Stripped from the earth as quickly as your will to stay. Part of me always hoped that I really was what you cared about. That despite the adoption records, my gray-blue eyes really were the product of yours. Our storm cloud colored eyes foreshadowing our thunderous arguments. Maybe the beauty I find in the dark gray clouds now represents my love for you. Or the strength I see in myself for standing up to you.

*

I'll always remember our storms. Our spiteful, sharp, utterly hostile words. The way we aimed to kill in the heat of an argument and how you taught me to not back down. Now, the once peaceful, calm little girl you aspired to have has grown into a spitfire, caring, strong woman. You taught me how to remain calm when

I'm burning with rage and how to identify everything I don't want in a future partner. You taught me how to not be. You taught me how to handle hardship. For that, I thank you.

*

We've never been any kind of calm. But I don't know any other way. I wish that there was a way I could tell you, that despite our past, I will always be your littlest Rae. I will always remember the way you carried me on your shoulders and the way you sang your silly little songs. The memories will always remain. Good and bad. And while I carry all of this, I know that you're there for me. I know that if I came to you right now, if I finally called you, you'd be there. You'd tell me what I need, or want, to hear and you'd be on the other side of the line. I don't know how I'm supposed to let go of you. Maybe I'll call your non-existent number and wait for you to ask how your Little Rae is today. Until one day I realize I really am the last one standing and will face the storm of my future all by myself. Storms pass, it's true, I just always thought ours would last forever.

THESE PAGES ARE ALSO FILLED WITH STARS
by Kendra Couturier
St. Mary School - Lake Leelanau, 10th Grade

For Beginning.

This is a beginning,

It is pages. Pages filled with words.
Words filled with truth,
Maybe some lies,
And also some hope,
some laughter, love, and light.
Some raw and endless emotion, along with sadness
maybe.
And stars.
These pages are also filled with stars.

It will be both a battle cry and a song.
But we do not know yet, do we?

This is an ending,
But it is also a beginning.

Sleepwalking.

I did not think of stars.
I did not think of any large number of uncountable things,
I didn't even think of any number of finite things that were
    important,
whatever that meant.

I did not think of the number two-thousand three-hundred
    sixty-three.
Nor drowning in a sea of tears.
Death and dying.
I did sometimes.

Sometimes, also, I thought of laughter,
skipping and twirling through life.
I held joy tangible,
luminous.
A star.
But not then.
I thought of nothing to tear my heart into a thousand tiny pieces
    and nothing to stitch it back together.

Instead,
Sleep, sleepwalking through a day a hundred days a thousand
    days an infinite number of days.
I did not count.
Instead,
Tapping, thumbs sliding up, a hundred scrolls a thousand scrolls
    an infinite number of scrolls on glass webbed with tiny cracks.
I did not count.

I did not think of stars,
I did not think of any large number of infinite things,
Drowning in white noise and distraction and forgetting.
Until something ripped,
and I was wakened from my numb sleep. Everything
flooded through the seam.

Now,
I thought of stars.
I did not count.
I was only filled with wonder
And delight.

More than a Sunset.

Sun gold blazed
on the glass windows across the lake,
So dazzling that it must have cracked and dripped its honeyed
    nectar
on the sliver of land unshadowed
as the sun dipped below the horizon,
Forever on its path.

People gathered on the tiny square of a front step, laughing
    about some mutually understood thing.
The world sharpened into focus.
And suddenly
Or maybe not so suddenly
Everything clicks and the world is expanding

And it was beautiful.

we will never be here at this
moment
in time again

And then it was over.
The windows were extinguished to mere
thin gray glass
in the half-dark.
The wind whipped
up to some unguessable speed.

Morning came,
And all I was left with was a single pale memory.

Cemetery Flowers.

Winter is coming.
They stride in a slow procession down the rows of stones,
pulling out the
plastic-stemmed roses
thin petaled and
thornless
Planters of frosted over flowers come down,
untangling vines from shepherd's hooks.

Solemn, somber,
a once evergreen wreath
for someone's mother, grandmother, aunt, friend,
pinned
by long rusty pins
disintegrating as it is detached from the earth
it already lay buried under one winter's snowy blanket,
one more would not do.

How strange it is
undecorating these memorials,
undoing loving hands' tender work and thoughtful placement,
heart
break
ing.

Armfuls upon armfuls
Of flowers, real and artificial, dead and dying,
An explosion of color and love,
placed in the back of a truck, once decorating someone's final
    resting place,
now delivered to their own.

The elements are too strong,
beauty is fleeting, life is fragile.
That is how it is.
We are past the point of no return.
Winter must come.

p.s. We will be back in the spring with new flowers.

THE SHROUDED WOODS

by Oliva Craker

Suttons Bay High School, 10th Grade

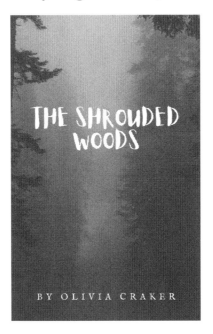

As I lay on the old, weathered couch my headache hung over me heavily. I groaned. Unfortunately, it was a common occurrence. I always seemed to be able to forget how it felt until I was going through it once more. Now that I was sweating uncontrollably, I, to my dismay, remembered the repulsive feeling of it. Of being both cold and hot at the same time. The sweating, the confusion. I slung an arm over the edge of the couch, brushing the lip of a bottle with my fingertips. A sickening stench had flushed the clear air right out of the room.

I sighed and craned my head to glance out the large window to my side. Through my heavy eyes, I caught the sight of the lowering sun, its golden haze fading into a rich orange beyond the horizon, staining the walls of the cabin. The leaves whipped mercilessly against one another, fighting and tearing clean off of some of their stems in the brew of wind and rain.

Glancing away, my eyes hooked onto the lantern above the wooden table to my right—behind the couch. Simple yet fitting to the simplistic decor of the rustic cabin. The fireplace, old and made of cracked stone, sat a few lengths away at my feet. A crooked mantle hung over its edge. Odd trinkets adorned it: little skulls, glass bottles, tins, and a small wooden carving of some creature I didn't recognize—however, it seemed vaguely familiar for some strange reason. Taking in the rest of my surroundings, through my mind still thick as mud, I realized something.

I knew exactly where I was.

And frankly, I didn't want to think about why I was here.

My eyelids fell time after time, and I shook my head every few moments to fight off my desire for sleep. My head pulsed again as I tried craning it towards the door, making me yelp. The door sat behind me, just out of my sight. I grumbled. If I could have, I would've sat up, yet my body failed me time and time again. I needed water—desperately. A shaky, exhausted breath huffed through me, the air choked and heavy. I needed *her*.

I called out her name. No answer.

Again, louder this time—no answer.

With each passing moment, my head spun and spun. I kept calling out her name for what felt like minutes on end—hours on end. The only response was the howling wind, heaving outside the rickety walls. My breathing slowed, my lungs filling breath after breath with the sharp—yet putrid—cabin air. My bare forearms lay dormant beneath the thin blanket pulled just above my shoulders. She was always so good to me. Her sweet voice echoed in my ears, giving me a sense of relief from the nausea forming from within.

I love you, darling. You know I do. I'm always here for you. Don't worry so much...

I called out her name again, chasing those honeyed whispers and doing so until my breathing complemented the pace of my pounding heart.

The warmth of the blanket coddled me as I shifted into consciousness once more. Outside, darkness still enveloped the forest. Its coat of black so dark that the night seemed to hum. The strong breeze, I realized, had vanished—yet my headache lingered. The stench of the cabin remained intact.

The leaves of the dense forest shivered with the slight wind. As if they were trying to cuddle together now, seeking warmth in one another's vessels of fading green.

I slowly—and carefully—swung my feet over the edge of the couch, pulling the blanket up around my shoulders to avoid the bite of the cabin's air. That's when I really felt it. The weakness, the nausea, the aching that could be felt not only within muscle, but in the bone. It all seemed to crash over me at once. My hand traveled up the back of my neck and into my scruffy hair as I stared into the night. The more I stared, the more uneasy I became. An odd, twisting feeling caught in my gut and I couldn't register why. I was supposed to wake in the morning, not only a few hours after falling asleep.

What had woken me up?

I rose to my weakened feet, tucking the blanket between my folded arms as I started to walk away. However, I couldn't. That window kept me there, my eyes scanning the darkness between every tree. Every bush. Every branch. I couldn't move. I couldn't rip my eyes away. Why?

Finally, after minutes, with dread hanging above my shoulders, I managed to cut the odd tension between me and the outside world. I shook slightly, clutching the blanket closer to me. I felt better than before, but the world was still unstable. Stepping over to the counter across the room, I turned the handle to the sink and poured myself a glass of water. I tried to make sense of it all. Was there something out there? Were the stories true? I eyed the odd wooden carving on the mantle of the fireplace. A small shiver crawled its way down my neck. I brought the glass to my lips but hesitated, tasting the coldness that radiated from the ice on the roof of my mouth.

A singular pair of boots sat on the floor—my boots. One coat hung on the door. One suitcase lay on the bed tucked into the remaining corner of the room. I was alone. The items scattered throughout the room said as much. My wife was not here with me.

My blood ran cold at the memory. I gulped, chills surfing through my veins on waves of horror. The flames in the fireplace were no more, reduced to nothing but ash now. The cabin was noticeably colder, the stench of alcohol still hanging in the air. I was still struggling to accept reality: she was dead.

I tried to push the flashbacks of her down, down, down into the depths of my soul. I could still hear her whimpering. I could still see her body, once full and strong, deteriorate under the covers of that too-white bed. Could still see her beautiful, deep-set hazel eyes fill with tears as we shared memories with one another, memories we would never be able to treasure together again. Her crying echoed through me, snagging a choked sob from somewhere deep inside of my smoke-damaged lungs. I felt the softness of her hands envelop mine, her porcelain skin stark against my calloused palms. The ring I had given her... I could still feel the carefully-crafted gem underneath the pad of my finger.

Shaking, I set the glass down on the countertop with a *clink*. I wondered if it was loud enough to wake the world outside. The ice floated gently, slowly melting inside of the still water as I clasped my palms together, remembering her touch. Coming here was a mistake. Too many memories had been made with her here.

My eyes lingered on a bottle of pills that had been laid carefully on the dining table. A damaged table, worn down by years and years of blissful parties and weekend retreats. A table my parents and their friends used to sit around, dealing cards and drinking rum. Sharing stories together and freaking us young children out with a tale about the monster in the woods. No chairs surrounded it anymore. Broken glass and thick-smelling liquid lay sprawled over the top, agony hiding behind every drop and jagged shard. Bottles on bottles. I sighed, the hollowness of it—the sombreness—fogged up the room, and laid like a boulder on my chest. Even heavier than the alcohol-ridden air, or my lingering hangover. Who knows how long I'd been here, now. Weeks? Just to drink my problems away again because I couldn't stand seeing her clothing neatly laid out on her side of the bed any longer.

I tried pushing everything down. The memory of her, her voice, why I'd come here. I prayed my mind would finally start being good to me. Prayed the guilt away. The thoughts, the urges, the emptiness... Yet to no avail. Since she was gone, I was fog and mist; rain and sorrow. I was nothing without her. Nothing at all. This cabin was mine now. Passed down through generation after generation in my family. A family that grew apart long ago. Now that my lover was gone, I had no one left to love me. No one left I could love, either. Living seemed unnecessary in my contorted mind.

And then I heard a scream.

A woman's scream, outside in the groaning woods.

My legs grew stiff. Had I heard it right? Hesitantly, I walked toward the picture window. My feet padded on the wooden floor, my thick socks blessing my feet with a cat's stealth as that window grew nearer, nearer. Shrugging the blanket off my shoulders, I gripped the window sill tentatively and stared out into the darkness. The soft fabric fell gently behind my ankles. If the *clink* of glass on the countertop hadn't woken the outside world, maybe my pulsing heart did.

And then another wail of terror flooded my ears again, closer this time.

Before I even knew what I was doing, my boots were on and a jacket was slung around the dip in my arm. I flew through the door and dashed out into the stormy night.

I ran and ran, branches and bushes threatening to make me drop with every stride I took. The gentle swaying of the dark leaves hovered above me like ghosts, taunting and teasing me with every movement my body made. I had grown so out of shape the past year. Maybe my body, too, was deteriorating. Just like hers had started to after the accident. After everything happened, I stopped trying. I stopped *wanting* to try. I weaved in between two large trees—giants in comparison to those around them— and dodged stray roots. The crisp night air was a toxic haze in my throat, icing the inner layer of my lungs with the scent of wet leaves.

I keeled over, my breaths ragged and rough from inhaling the wind. I hurled up my guts within seconds after stopping. The dead leaves beneath my feet squished slightly, soggy from the ongoing hours of rain. Slowly, I steadied my breaths. I needed to keep going, to save whoever was out here.

I could not stop. I *would* not stop. Not again.

Another wail sounded from my left, a little softer now. It sounded more like a whimper than anything. I wiped the corner of my mouth on a wet sleeve.

Feeling the rain drip down my exposed neck, I tilted my head in the direction of the noise, my hair shielding one of my eyes.

And there lay a fox, bloodied and tattered, in the damp undergrowth of the sullen forest. Slowly, I tip-toed toward him, making a conscious effort not to startle the poor creature. Stepping over a puddle of mud and into the small clearing, I finally caught sight of his face—blessed by the gentle kiss of the moon. She sat high in the sky, darkened clouds around her yet none shielding the light. Rain padded against the fox's reddish fur, dripping down around his eyes with a contrasting tenderness to his circumstance. His blackish toes lay sprawled in the mud, tense and shaking. Shaking... Shaking...

Our eyes met, and I had never seen a creature so afraid. He watched me with pulled-back ears, and I watched him back. A brew of awe and empathy coursed its way through my veins. He made no sound now—no more wails or shrieks. Water dripped down my neck and onto the skin beneath my coat, sending a chill through my body—one that I felt crawl its way into the marrow of my bones. Then, I peered at the rest of him. Another chill ruptured its way through me. But this time, not from the rain. A glint of yellowish-white edged into my vision. His bone lay exposed to the cold air, crimson fluid staining his leg fur a dull shade of red. The shade of suffering and pain. The injured fox caught eyes with me again; his disheartened expression weaving a splinter of rawness into my heart.

What was I to do?

Rocks, logs, and branches rimmed and filled the small clearing in the trees. Small mushrooms and crawling insects fed off of them, gaining nutrients amongst the flora. I stared at the fox, not a word rolling off of my tongue. I felt the rain increase, and with it came a *boom* of thunder. And again, I asked myself: *what was I to do?* The leaves on the trees whipped together once more, and I couldn't help but wish I was back in that muggy cabin. Away from the dark, the rain, the moon's glare. But I had come out here...and for what, again? Another *boom* of thunder, another chill.

Noticing a stone near my foot, I reached down to grasp it in my palm. I studied it for a moment, the sharp dips and curves engraving themselves into my mind, before glancing at the fox. Then back at the stone. Then back at him again. His eyes shone more dully than before, clouded from whatever was going on in his innocent mind. His shaking increased, perhaps from the rain, perhaps from my presence. Despite the short distance between us, my legs were still like pillars in the mud. The stone trembled in my hand. He was in so much pain. As rain seeped into my scalp, I gulped, gripping the rock a fraction tighter. Not nearly enough to prepare my head—and my heart—for what I had to do.

Hours seemed to pass as I stood there, staring at him, noticing the way the rain poured down his worn face. Finally, after gathering a sliver of courage, I tentatively approached the fox. His ears pinned back so far I swore they might break off. I had never been this close to something so wild before. His head shrunk back into his neck as he examined me from below. About twelve inches; so close. He was an animal that was once free but no longer had the strength to continue on. My nails scraped against the rough plane of the stone, the feeling vibrating into my fingertips as I watched the raindrops hit his nose. One after another. *Drop... Drop... Drop...* My coat had only been able to protect me for so long, so I too felt the effects of the rainfall. The shivering, the odd dampness trapped beneath layers of fabric, even the emotional misery. All of it in a cruel brew accompanied by a garnish of gut-wrenching dread.

I brought the stone above my head.

And with a choked sob, brought it down upon him.

He suffered no more.

In that moment, I wished that I could end my suffering as well.

What had even caused his wound? It had to be large if it could break his bone. If it could leave him so tattered and terrified. I grimaced at the body of the fox, now alleviated from his misery. As far as my knowledge went, there were no natural predators of foxes around here. Unless...

I whipped my head around to scan every edge of the clearing. To drink in as many details as possible in the dreary conditions. Every shadow, every noise sounding different than rain, every breath of wind whipping through the swaying trees—I fought against the effects of my hangover. Suddenly, I became keenly aware of the fact that if something did indeed come after me, I could not defend myself. I felt each pocket just to make sure. Unfortunately, I was correct. No weapon, no flashlight, no...nothing. If only I hadn't been so hungover, then maybe I would have grabbed something—anything—as I dashed out into the night. *Something* I could use to protect myself against the monster haunting the old tale from when I was a young boy—if it was even real.

My gut started to churn, twisting my organs together as I felt an odd presence drawing near the clearing. I adjusted my weight on wobbly knees, unable to bring myself to look behind me. Pain edged its way into my head, poking and prodding. I, too, was now shivering from something other than the rainwater. As my headache worsened, so did the dread within me. I couldn't stand it anymore. I turned my head away from the direction of the fox ever-so-slightly. There, intermingled with the undergrowth, was something shadowed and still. Eyes—fixed on me. I fought against the acid in my stomach, trying to keep it down. As the creature crept forward, I noticed its gray teeth and dark gums—rotten and vile. Gums that would be stained red if I didn't move. Teeth that could tear me apart. Maybe letting it eat me wouldn't be so bad after all. I would see my wife again, maybe even have a purpose again. As I pondered those thoughts, it crept closer.

And closer.

And closer. Only enough, however, to where its head was partially poking out of the undergrowth. Just enough to where I could fully see the length of its teeth and its brow. Its furry head looked familiar; it was similar to that carving on the mantle. Horror struck my gut like a punch as I realized... The stories were true.

It lunged.

I ran.

Darting through the forest, I choked on air. My feet pounded into the mud and undergrowth, each step taken recklessly and fueled by adrenaline and terror. The throb in my head turned into a splitting pain. Heaving, and gasping, and choking on rain... I kept on running through whatever muscle soreness I could still feel beneath the adrenaline. I hurtled over a root jutting out from a large oak tree, nearly catching my toes on the edge. I heard the creature crashing through the bushes behind me, getting nearer and nearer with every stride. It would continue to get closer until I could feel its hot breath on my calves. I kept running.

I stumbled behind a cluster of small trees. A wet branch awaited me there, swiping across my face and making me cry out. My hands flared outwards, frantically shoving away the rain-coated leaves as I ducked under the limbs. Rain coated my brow and slid down into my eye. I winced, swiping it away mid-lunge as I dashed between more clusters of trees. Over bushes and roots. At that point, I didn't even know where I was, or where I was headed. All that mattered was getting away. All that mattered was escaping the teeth and claws of the thing that threatened my life.

There was nothing left for me at home, my family had dispersed or passed on long ago. There was nobody left to care for me—or for me to care for. I felt a throb of longing inside of my chest as I weaved around a large rock, deciding not to step on—or over—it in case I fell; the first semi-coordinated move I made in my sprint so far. I didn't have a life to return to. I barely even had a life to save.

So why was I running?

I abruptly came to a creek. My feet scrambled at the edge, kicking dull pebbles into the barely-visible liquid as I scrambled to a stop. Unfortunately for me, the darkness prevented me from seeing how wide it was, so there was no way to jump over it. The moon hadn't shown her face for some time now. Not since the rain began to pick up again. She was covered by darkened clouds that were filled with rage. Another *boom* raced across the sky, which sent me running once again, more cautiously now that I was aware of the creek. A growl sounded through the air. Too close now to provide me with any hope of survival. Yet like a deer in a chase, I continued onward, crashing through branches and bushes to save my life.

Sopping wet and miserably chilled, I unzipped my hefty jacket, my pace slowing down from my draining endurance. I cradled it underneath my elbow, praying that my joints would now be more mobile. The rain dripped from the tightly-woven fabric onto my legs as I jogged, though I was too wet to care. I hadn't heard from the creature since the creek. Maybe it had finally given up and gone back to whatever dark cave it resided in. I hoped as much. My lungs grew heavy and tight, forcing me to stumble to a stop at the base of a pine. Wasn't I just in a deciduous forest? I scanned my surroundings for any signs of civilization, yet to no avail. The lights from my cabin weren't in sight, nor was the road. The needles on the ground coated the forest floor, providing a deafened cushion as I took a moment to catch my breath while trotting amongst the trees. Large, spiky pines towered over me. Hundreds of years old. Wise, old ones like the ones in children's stories.

And then, a growl erupted from between the trunks. Images of my deceased wife flashed through my mind as claws raked into my skin. How she fought to live, yet failed. I cried out, bashing my fist backward into what was probably the jaw of the creature. A gut-wrenching snarl was the only response I got. I flipped over, bringing my knees up to my chest as it snapped down at me, its darkened gums and hazel eyes mere inches above my head. Drool fell upon my forehead as I bashed at its throat and face with whatever I could. My hands, my feet, and a rock I had picked up moments earlier when I had fallen.

She fought. Fought for me, for herself. For us. I saw her eyes in the eyes of the monster as it killed me slowly, painfully. What had I been doing all this time? I wasn't gonna die. Not unless I went down swinging. I needed to live for her, to try. I didn't want to lose like this. I *wasn't* gonna die. A flash of gold slammed into the creature above me, knocking it onto the forest floor. Howling, barking, and snarling ripped through the night. Everything went black.

Not tonight.

Ten years later, I sit around the fire. My dog, Jane, is cuddled up around my feet. Her golden fur shines in the firelight, soft and comforting. A laugh sounds from behind me, echoing from the hallway. The noise of it cradles my soul. Gentle arms wrap around my neck from behind before a kiss lands on my cheek. She hums, nosing my ear before swinging around the couch to join me. Intertwining our hands, she tells me about her day. Her ups and downs. About her job, her parents, all of it. I could listen to her talk for hours. Her voice is sweeter than honey and never fails to ease me. Jane shifts, rolling to her side and exposing her belly to the fire. My wife of six years reaches down to pet her, humming and twiddling her fingers in Jane's soft fur.

Moments later, two small bodies barrel out from the hallway, squeaking and giggling. My wife shoots up from the couch, scolding our children gently. Jane pops her head up and wags her tail, gentle eyes fixed on the youngest child. My wife takes their tiny hands and begins to lead them back to their room, much to the children's dismay. However, my youngest breaks from his mother's grasp and flings himself onto my lap. His mother calls out after him, yet I only chuckle, the sound a noticeably-clearer rumble in my lungs. Had been clear ever since I survived that night in the forest. I stopped a lot of things since that night—started a lot too. With a gentle squeeze, I let my son return to his mother. She gives me a dismissing wave before finally returning them to their room. I reach down and pat Jane on her head then bring a hand up to my freshly-shaved face. As I look out the window, more memories of that night appear in my mind.

I lived. Not without the help of Jane. I drum my fingers on her head and she wags her tail. Her scar caught my eye, large, and raked across her side. Where she came from had been a mystery, still was. I was just grateful she got there in time. That she became a physical presence worth living for, just like my family is to me now.

Here I am, with a family and a home. Here I am, finally looking forwards and not backward anymore. Remembering my late wife, I smile.

Here I am, alive.

FALLING LEAVES

by Sydney Flaherty
Traverse City Central High School, 12th Grade

By Sydney Flaherty

There were no windows in the room and bleach hung in the air, sticking to the room's sharp corners and the rubber soles of the three patients' shoes. It was suffocating. They sat on white plastic chairs, awaiting instructions with burning lungs.

Over the past days, they had been pricked and tested, drowning in scantron sheets and TB tests. But now it was the finale. In the corner, on a lone metal cart were three identical glasses each three-quarters of the way filled with water. Next to the glasses were two identical-looking men. They wore blue slippers over their white shoes and stiff lab coats over their button-up shirts; the only difference was that the man on the right held a small metal tray.

The tray was not fancy, it did not have any carvings on it or any interesting patterns. It was cold and plain and held three perfectly spaced white pills. The pills were oval and no larger than the tip of your pinky finger, they were decorated with a single line down the middle, like a scar. The man on the left lifted each pill with small tweezers held by a gloved hand. One would expect the pills to leave small crumbs on the tray as they were lifted up, yet once they were gone it's like they were never there.

Each pill was dropped into a glass of water. The patients watched the pills fall in slow motion, secreting white dust and clouding the glass. The man on the right checked his watch. One minute passed, two minutes. It would have been completely silent if not for the sizzling of the pills, it was the kind of noise that feels like it's in your ear. The kind of noise that buzzes inside of you.

Five minutes later the man on the right looked at the man on the left and they brought a glass to each patient. The glasses were lukewarm and a dull white color where there once was cool, clear, water.

The patients drank all at once, the room filled with the sound of moving water and a chorus of gulping. The liquid should not have tasted like anything, it should have felt like warm air filling their mouths and moving downward. The patients took short breaks between gulps and felt the eyes of the two men on them, examining.

Once they were done the glasses looked clean, there was no white powdery residue left like sugar at the bottom of a mug of tea. The man on the left collected the glasses one by one and left.

They already knew the information they needed to know, but the man on the right was more paranoid than the man on the left and stayed. He relayed the information the patients had already read and signed on to, the same information he had given them before they entered the windowless room. They had just taken a psychoactive drug, it would take time before it reached its full effects, probably two days, be careful and make sure you have someone watching you at all times, report back here at 1:00 pm on Friday when we will administer more tests, thank you for helping us find new ways to combat serious health issues, your government and fellow citizens applaud you.

The patients filed out one by one.

...

When Carlos gets back from the experiment, he eats Oreos for dinner on his college-supplied desk, right next to his computer with the cracked screen that's always almost dead.

He falls asleep a few hours later, surrounded by a green hue emitted from the LED lights his roommate wrapped around the corner between the walls and the ceiling. Carlos dreams of nothing and forgets to set his alarm for nine.

Sun streams into the dorm room and for a second Carlos forgets about the time or the fact that he has a class at ten. When he does remember, he groans and checks his phone: 11:00 am. Carlos does not freak out like many would in his place; instead he decides there's no point and pulls his comforter over his head to block out the light. Carlos feels slightly happy that he slept in, he hates the class anyway. Next semester, he tells himself, he will not sign up for any classes before noon or maybe before 1 pm; he falls asleep before he can decide on the specifics.

Carlos gets up again at 12:30 pm. He grabs a Coca-Cola from his roommate's minifridge and drinks it while he gets dressed and combs his hair. He leaves the can on his desk as he walks out of the room.

The hallway is exactly what you'd expect of a subpar state school with no redeeming qualities besides its basketball team, which is surprisingly good. It takes ten minutes for Carlos to walk to the building for his first class and another one to find his seat: the fifth from the aisle in the third row. Carlos always sits in this seat and all of his friends sit in the seats around it, he likes the routine for the stability it provides.

Today, however, a guy with bright orange hair and a piercing in one ear is sitting in Carlos' friend Blake's seat. Carlos is not a confrontational guy and so he doesn't ask the guy to move or question if he's new to the class.

"Carlos! Yo, where's Mike?" It's the orange haired guy and he's asking about Carlos' roommate.

"Uh, he's visiting family in, uh, I think, Missouri."

"Oh chill." This guy has the same vocabulary as Blake: slang words people used in middle school.

"Sorry, do I know you?"

The redhead laughs, "Yo, are you, like, on drugs right now? You're staring at me weird." He's starting to pick up on the fact that Carlos is genuinely confused, "Bro, it's Blake, what's going on with you?"

Carlos starts to laugh, it's a prank, this whole thing is funny and pretty soon the redhead is going to give up the act and start laughing too but right now his face is twisted into some expression of concern and confusion. Another guy walks up, he has a large brown beard and round glasses. He sits right next to Carlos.

"Hey guys, I don't think Liam's gonna be here on time, Pete told me he was asleep like 30 minutes ago."

"This is so funny guys," Carlos is laughing really hard now, then he looks at the guy with the beard "how do you know Liam anyway?"

The guy with the orange hair is turning an unhealthy shade of white and seems to be staring down the bearded guy, pleading for help. The guy with the beard laughs but Carlos can tell it's forced. "Dude, I'm Ben, I've known Liam since like freshman year, you've known *me* since freshman year!" He's smiling now and so Carlos smiles too.

"Oh yeah, Ben and Blake who I'm sitting right next to, the ones I've known for years. So funny," Carlos can tell he's not making sense but he rationalizes it with the fact that nothing is making sense right now.

Finally, the professor walks in. She is one of Carlos' favorite professors and he actually enjoys listening to her lectures. But, the man who walks in is not his professor. Maybe he is some sort of surprise guest speaker?

"Let's get started," the man says in a raspy tone.

"Dude, I hate this professor, this class is always so boring," the guy with orange hair says under his breath, trying to move on from the incident seconds earlier.

Carlos' mind is racing now, it's one thing for his friends to have planned some extremely intricate prank but for them to somehow rope in the professor? It's not possible.

Before he can convince himself not to, Carlos is pacing down the steps and making his way up to the "professor's" podium. Carlos' ears are ringing and he can't hear the guys with the orange hair and beard asking him what he's doing, or the professor as he asks if he's alright.

Carlos looks up into a sea of faces he's never seen before as they laugh and whisper, one girl calls out: "Carlos what are you doing?!" with a laugh.

"Who are you?" Carlos intends to yell it back at her but it comes out as a whisper. He feels nauseous, then he feels angry. "How do you know me?!" He's yelling now "Who are you?" he's not even asking anymore.

"Carlos, this is getting very disruptive. Please get some fresh air or return to your seat." It's the professor. Carlos leaves the class, staring at everyone's faces as he passes. He cannot recognize one.

The air outside feels good, fresh, and sterile. Carlos' mind is racing as he tries to rationalize what just happened, he won't accept the fact that he can't. Instead, he develops an experiment: At 10:00pm he will make his way to a party he heard about a few days ago. This party is sure to include at least ten people he knows and has talked to more than twice. It's pretty simple: if he recognizes the people, congratulations to Blake and Ben for pulling an amazing prank and somehow replacing the entire class with new people, if he doesn't recognize the people, well, maybe Blake and Ben are just playing a bigger and more intricate prank? Carlos is relying on the first option.

In his dorm, Carlos tries to watch Netflix but he can't focus, he's hungry but feels sick anytime he thinks about food. Carlos spends a few hours pacing the small dorm room and planning out what he'll text Blake and Ben when he recognizes someone at the party, it has to be witty but not super accusatory...he doesn't want to seem butthurt. But eventually, Carlos gets sick of even this and sits down at his desk.

The party is at an apartment about fifteen minutes away from his dorm but Carlos keeps up a fast pace, barely noticing his foggy breath as he walks through the cold dark. The party is warm and loud, and Carlos' brain moves to the beat. He welcomes the sounds of conversation and begins his experiment.

He walks slowly from corner to corner, room to room. He stares at each person intently, racking his brain for memories or really anything. He gets a few confused looks and even some "Hey Carlos"s which he hates, it's like they're taunting him: "Hey Carlos, bet you can't remember me but guess what? I remember you!"

He makes his way back to the front door without having recognized anyone, he circles through the whole apartment again, and then again. After twenty minutes Carlos resolves to stand at the door and greet people, after twenty minutes of this and five "Hey

Carlos"s Carlos begins to greet everyone not just with a smile but with a question: "Do you know me?"

Some of them say yes, others walk past him and laugh, many ask if he's okay, and one guy offers him money. In between greetings, Carlos watches the party. Everyone's moving so fast they blur together. Carlos wonders what's going on, what if it's not a prank? What if he's the problem? They talk and walk, and dance, and each movement looks synchronized and planned. Carlos has never been able to let go of himself, to surrender himself to the music and movement. He drowns instead, thrashing his arms all the way down.

A girl with her hair tied in a bun tries to make conversation with him, but Carlos cannot focus on her voice. "Carlos, you don't seem like your usual self." Even she knows something's wrong with him. Carlos feels the hot tears on his cheek before he realizes he's crying. Standing in the crowded apartment, Carlos has never felt more alone.

Carlos walks around aimlessly for probably two hours in the cold. His tears warm his face. He does not know what to do now, who to call or what to ask. There's one of two possibilities: everyone is playing a prank on him or he's gone mad and everyone knows it. Carlos is too exhausted to formulate an experiment or further analyze the situation. In all honesty, Carlos doesn't see the point. They all know he's a fraud, one way or the other.

It's funny because Carlos always knew his whole persona: the fun guy with friends and good social skills, was going to break eventually. He knew how fragile it was, one misstep and he was out. But he never thought he wouldn't know what he did wrong, he always thought he might be able to fix it if he tried hard enough.

Carlos' legs are numb, it feels like he's floating. He sits down.

Carlos can feel the bench vibrate slightly as the wind hits it. He watches as the leaves fall one by one along the courtyard. He likes how the leaves fall together, one couldn't recognize one leaf from the rest of them on the ground, and yearns for the anonymity they all share. He begs to be swept up by the world and the wind.

...

This time of year the sky is always gray and the air claws at red cheeks. Cecilia has emerged from the experiment and now wears a sweater, jeans, and a scarf. She can't feel the wind blowing on her. She is so warm she doesn't notice her white, smoky breath or the way her teeth are chattering in rhythm. To combat the change of season, Cecilia is armed with a rake. She has never used the rake and strings of dust wrap around the wires, they fly into the air.

The trees are bare and ugly and all their gray and brown leaves are on the ground, calling out and begging to be put back in place. Cecilia can't help them, they are dead.

This season is haunting Cecilia and following her around like a stalker. She wants to be rid of it. Cecilia wants to wash this year off her with a stone, scrubbing and scratching until the only thing that is left is bright red, oozing flesh, and clean blood.

The trees are screaming at Cecilia, "give them back to us," they are sobbing. She can remember when the trees were bright, vibrant with reds and oranges and yellows. Cecilia does not understand how something can be so beautiful as it dies so slowly, she is used to excess skin and sunken eyes. Did the trees know the leaves were preparing to die when they stood so proudly?

The leaves are not good and beautiful anymore; they faded and became brittle one morning when the sun had not yet risen. Cecilia wishes someone would have told her in advance, then she could have salvaged them in all their color and life.

The leaves are ugly and they distract from the green grass of summer and Cecilia wants them gone. She has a rake and she will dispose of them properly on the side of the road like her neighbors did last month.

And so she begins.

It is easy work, shoving the leaves together. Cecilia tells herself the trees are happy with her, a rightful burial for their lost children. Cecilia tells them "don't worry, they are in good hands" and consoles the unshakable trees above her.

Her hands are so cold they have frozen to the worn wooden handle of the rake, Cecilia doesn't notice this. She is thinking about a ceremony for the leaves. Cecilia once heard ancient Greeks used to burn their loved ones when they died, maybe she'll burn the leaves and scatter the ashes on the trees' roots.

It takes Cecilia about an hour to realize the ground is no more clean than when she started raking. Everything looks the same except for the pile of rotting leaves in the middle of her yard. She continues anyway.

Thirty minutes later and she still hasn't seen grass. As soon as she moves a row of leaves, more fall to take their place. Cecilia looks up but the trees are bare, she does not know where the leaves are coming from. She continues on.

They won't stop falling from the heavens, these phantom leaves replace their siblings before she can stop them. Cecilia moves the rake slowly, as soon as a leaf is moved, another is added before one can even recognize the grass below. Cecilia moves the rake fast, but not fast enough and the leaves match her pace.

Cecilia yearns for the grass because she knows she can't see it; she moves faster and faster. Her arms are heavy and taut, moving with a purpose they haven't had since last year. Her breathing matches the pace, unsteady and gasping. She clings to each movement with hope and is struck with disappointment anew each time the leaves fall.

Blisters are forming on her palms, and Cecilia is holding onto the rake like a life raft; it steadies her enough to keep going. She moves to each corner of the yard, each inch has been raked over and over yet there is nothing to show for it. Except for the ever-growing pile of dead leaves that now reaches above her yard's fence.

The leaves are no longer dead children to Cecilia, they are murderers she must catch. She cannot stop even though she wants to. Her body screams for water and food and rest but she is not listening. Her movements are becoming jerky and relentless, it is like she is killing something. Blood runs down the rake's handle like a river from her hands.

The wind is howling and its emptiness wills Cecilia to keep going. The trees are laughing at her; doesn't she know leaves grow, fall, and decompose? That this will happen no matter what she does?

Cecilia wants to scream at the trees and the wind and the gray clouds that block out the sun. She wants to tell them she isn't crazy, that leaves fall and people pick them up, and that if she does this she can stop the full, ugly death. She yells in a hoarse voice, "this is not up to you, I dictate when the leaves stop and where they go."

She is so busy yelling she doesn't notice the pile of leaves creeping up behind her. It happens so gradually that she can't feel their brittle edges as they caress her face and wipe her tears and sweat. She is looking down and therefore wouldn't know that the pile is beginning to block out the sky and the meager light it provided. Cecilia is tearing at the leaves, ripping them to shreds just to find more in their place when she realizes it is pitch black and warm and the wind is not hitting her like it had before.

Cecilia's warm breath ricochets off the walls of the pile and hits her face. Her hands hold the position of the rake but the rake itself is on the ground. Cecilia is frozen and surrounded by different tones of gray and brown death. It suffocates her.

She sits down and feels the leaves crinkle beneath her. She is gasping for air and her body feels as though it is made of wood. Everything aches. Cecilia notices that she is tired and hungry and restless; but, she stays here. Partly because she does not believe she can move if she tries, and partly because she is finally warm.

...

Clark opens his eyes on Wednesday. The day after he was experimented on. The first thing he sees is the popcorn ceiling above his bed. When Clark was younger, he used to wait for his eyes to adjust to the dark and stare at the popcorn ceiling. If he concentrated enough he could make it look like the protruding dots of paint were actually inverted, like little craters. Later on in life, Clark came to question the mechanics of popcorn ceilings, how could someone be painting a ceiling while paint was dripping all over them? He eventually decided to assume he misunderstood the process. It seemed improbable that paint would even stay on a ceiling, like, it would just drip and drip and drip until it was all on the ground, with nothing left on the ceiling.

From where he lay, Clark could just make out the top edge of the window in his room. White paint was chipping off the window sill and outlining the deep gray color the sky always seemed to be. Once every few minutes a leaf would fall past the window, most of them were brown but some were bright oranges and yellows.

Directly above Clark was a dark brown fan with a light in the middle of it. A thin metal string of beads fell from the light, functioning as the light's on/off switch. The fact the light/fan was above his bed was bad for two reasons: one, in order to turn the light on and off Clark had to climb on top of his bed to reach the string, as opposed to simply reaching up and pulling the string while standing up. Two, the fan/light could, hypothetically, drop onto his bed while Clark was sleeping, crushing him underneath its weight and rendering him severely injured. Yet again, Clark is reminded of his youth and how he used to refuse to fall asleep because he was terrified something would happen to him while his eyes were closed and he was vulnerable. Once, Clark had gone to a party where someone had decorated their fan with streamers hanging off the individual blades, during the night someone accidentally turned the fan on and all the streamers flew to the ground like the leaves outside, or the paint on a ceiling.

It took thirty minutes for Clark to realize he could not move.

Clark was getting bored lying on his back, his stomach was filling with a dull pain which normally meant he was hungry. Clark wasn't ready to get out of bed and decided the pain might be temporarily healed if he shifted onto his left side, his mom used to tell him this position would make it easier to sleep when he was sick and had a bad stomach ache.

Yet, he was still on his back. It took Clark a few seconds to realize this, that he hadn't in fact turned to his side. So, he tried again. This time, Clark could feel his muscles tense as he attempted to switch positions. Still nothing. He tried again and again and again.

Clark tried for maybe an hour, alternating between turning, bending a knee, and lifting an arm. He could do nothing but lay there. He even continued to try once he had already come to half accept the fact that he was frozen in place; he only stopped once his muscles grew tired and sore.

It was an hour after this discovery that Clark realized he could try to call out for help. Clark had lived alone for decades and had since his senior year of college when he moved into a small apartment. Even when he had lived with roommates, he was not the "yell out for help" type. Clark generally preferred to suffer in silence as opposed to adding extra stress on others. Although this initially sounds rather saintly, Clark was less concerned with troubling people than he was with embarrassing himself by admitting he needed help. He hated this about himself but he never made an attempt to improve upon it. Instead, he just hated himself more for not making an effort.

Clark took a deep breath, filling his lungs with the stale air of his bedroom. Then he screamed: "Help!" His voice was dull and worn as most are in the mornings; it slightly broke as it sounded out the "L" in the word.

Then suddenly, it dawned on him. He could move his mouth. He could move his mouth! Then why couldn't he move anything else? He couldn't even move his head or scrunch his eyebrows, but there he was screaming for help. It must be all in his head.

When he was younger, like most kids, Clark was told the story of the boy who cried wolf. Initially, Clark did not worry about this story, he was a shy kid and couldn't imagine why someone would voluntarily draw attention to themself. However, as he grew, the story began to follow him around. He worried that if he asked too many questions at school someone might think he wasn't taking the class seriously, that his questions were his fault.

Eventually, he began to question his intentions, maybe he was just a terrible guy who liked to trick people and make them miserable. He grew to accept the possibility that he was really a selfish, manipulative person pretending to be normal as part of some trick that had yet to reveal itself. He would gain people's trust just to let them down by revealing his true self. Maybe this paralysis was just his way of drawing attention to himself, of calling people near him just to hurt them.

Clark tends to spiral. That is why he keeps himself busy with work and hobbies and parties he doesn't want to go to.

Clark could not pick up his phone to check the time but inferred it was probably around 9:00am. People would be at work, or getting to work, or talking to family members, and dropping kids off at school. Clark should have been at work by now.

If he yelled again, no one would hear. They were all busy. Except for maybe Clark's neighbor, an eccentric middle aged woman who seemingly did not have a job. He rakes the leaves in her yard every year. She is always at home and could maybe hear him if he shouted loud enough. Clark stopped himself, she was old and probably had hearing loss or would be extremely exhausted having to walk over to his house. But maybe she could do it.

Clark took another breath, preparing himself for a loud yell. But wait. What would she think, this old woman, after struggling through the cold over to his house, maneuvering in through the back door he always kept unlocked that creaked and bent when opened, finally locating his room, just to discover him. A man claiming he could not move while very clearly moving his mouth.

She would think he was tricking her. How cruel does one have to be to make an old woman feel like that? How cruel must he be? He won't do it.

Clark held his breath and stayed still. He would try to sleep, maybe once he woke up he would be able to move more than just his mouth. Crisis averted, what had he been thinking, calling for help? All he needed was sleep. It was all in his head.

It took Clark an hour to fall asleep, he couldn't get comfortable. Once he was finally sleeping, Clark dreamed of people with solemn faces pointing at him. They were judging him and shaking their heads acting like he was a criminal. Clark opened his eyes and felt guilty.

Doctor Venser had spent the last month administering experiments just like the one he had administered on Tuesday; he should be used to it by now. But something about the room they ushered the patients into with its fluorescent lights and blank walls still made him squirm. And the silence! His coworker, Doctor Milney, never seemed bothered by it but Doctor Venser couldn't keep still with all the patients looking at him and awaiting direction; he hated that he could give them anything and they wouldn't question it, but rather go along so obediently. It had been Doctor Milney's idea to administer the drugs in groups of threes. It made sense for the experiment, so Doctor Venser didn't argue but he secretly wished they could have done them all at once, like ripping off a band-aid.

The lack of humanity was mind-boggling, these people becoming lab rats. Normally, he could ignore it but this time Doctor Venser went off-script. What really did it was the young boy, college-aged, who had been so calm and cool throughout the earlier evaluations. He kept on shifting in his seat and wouldn't make eye contact with anyone. In his file, Doctor Venser had noted how the boy's father had died of something this drug might have been able to cure; he couldn't remember exactly what, and how the boy charmed the lady at reception when he first signed up for the experiment with talk about his favorite classes at university. Doctor Venser even remembered who had picked the boy up after the experiment: Ben Ferle, and how close they seemed.

But when he really thought about it, it was also the woman who made him so uncomfortable. Doctor Venser had heard she had participated in many experiments like this one; someone said she was some lonely, crazy old woman but Doctor Milney had heard and shut them up immediately. Doctor Venser also recalled how she had broken down crying while he was interviewing her in one of the earlier evaluations. It took him several minutes to decipher what she was talking about. She had been telling him about her only daughter who had died of pancreatic cancer a few months before. Doctor Venser questioned if she was in the right state of mind to participate, but deferred to Doctor Milney, who kept her on. On Tuesday, her words kept on repeating in Doctor Venser's head and he couldn't help but feel guilty for not being more vocal about his concerns.

And then, of course, there was the man. He seemed about the same age as the woman and always uncomfortable. During the evaluations when Doctor Venser had asked about his motivation for signing up the man had made some remark about the payment but Doctor Venser suspected it was one of those mid-life-crisis decisions made by people so desperate for change they'd do anything. But the man was quiet and definitely didn't seem like someone whose life was spiraling out of control. In fact, among the three participants, he always seemed the most put together. Situated in perfectly ironed business attire, saying thank you, and always arriving at least five minutes early. Even during the experiment, the man kept this up. In truth, it was the way he so casually drank the liquid and how patiently he sat that really scared Doctor Venser; he seemed so detached from his actions.

The three of them seemed almost like a family, gathered all together for dinner as opposed to a drug trial. Doctor Venser hadn't failed to notice that all their names started with a "C" or that they all lived within a five-mile radius of each other. He stayed up at night wondering if they had ever run into each other before the experiment or seen the same leaves as they fell to the ground every autumn if their connection could have been stronger than meeting once in a windowless lab.

Doctor Venser knew when he signed up for the job that this study would take years, and that this was just the beginning of many more experiments. Most of the time he was happy about it, happy to be making a positive change in the medical world. But in that room with the suffocating silence and desperate people, Doctor Venser regretted everything, questioning if any of it was really worth it.

He spent the time between Tuesday and Friday at 1:00pm wallowing in these feelings and trying to decipher their roots. What truly made him uncomfortable was how normal the people were. Of course, that's the point of an experiment, a representative sample. But these people seemed exactly like anyone else, a little weird or off-putting, but painstakingly normal nonetheless. They reminded Doctor Venser of himself, of everyone.

It was this normalness that led Doctor Venser to his decision, not insanity or malintent like Doctor Milney would go on to accuse. He knew he would get kicked off the experiment (he came to view this as an advantage) and he also knew that it would not doom the entire study, just a section.

Doctor Venser wouldn't be able to go through with the experiment if he didn't change something, wouldn't be able to hand the participants glasses filled with a substance that could hurt them. Looking them in the eyes as they drank poison.

And so Monday night, under a starless sky, the pills were exchanged with placebos.

...

Three people sat in a windowless room on plastic chairs under fluorescent lights. So close they could have reached out and touched each other. Residue from sugar pills still clinging to their throats.

None of them returned at 1:00pm on Friday.

MS. ROSALYN'S ATTIC OF SOULS
by Sela Geraci
Leland Public School, 11th Grade

My car bumps along the potholed road, hopping and dipping even at a crawling pace. It's almost spring, that mix of sun and snow that everyone who's lived in a northern climate knows. The snow has melted just enough to see the road and to unleash another year's worth of potholes upon unsuspecting drivers. I grimace as I see an upcoming one, one that's the size of half the road and at least four inches deep, and I hit it head-on. My whole car drops down, then up and continues to bounce along after passing through the crater in the road.

I'm headed to a private viewing of a house that my wife found in the pile of handouts and business cards of houses for sale that a friend of a friend had gathered and sent to us. My wife was offered her dream job, which involves moving up to this god-forsaken land of winter, and so we're up here for a few days, each of us taking half of the houses on our list of possible houses. So here I am, on a miserable road of potholes, headed to see one of the houses.

I pull into a driveway that is just as bad as the roads with spiderweb cracks that look like shattered glass and park my car in front of a large house with a rust orange facade. It would look somewhat grand if not for the junk piled around against the walls. Stacks of black metal fencing lean against birdbaths and eccentric statues. A blue-tinted statue melting horse that looks like wax left out in the sun too long, some gnome-looking creatures that look a little too much like they're staring into your soul with their mischievous smiles, and an upside-down mermaid, are all haphazardly placed around the house. There's also a pole covered in small brass bells that stands next to the front steps.

With a sigh, I get out of my car and walk up to the house, locking my car behind me.

As I knock on the door, the sun is getting ready to set behind me. The old lady who lives here insisted that if we were really interested in having a private showing, then we wouldn't mind coming later in the evening and keeping an old lady company for dinner, would we? It has been such a long time since she's had the chance to cook for anyone. I agreed since there really isn't a way to say no to a lonely old lady.

The door opens, and a weathered face framed by wispy white hair stares up at me and smiles. She's wearing a black dress and holding the ends of a lacey black shawl around her shoulders. Even her slippers are black.

"Oh, you must be Jeremy Caddel. Come in, come in!" she said, her voice frail and whispery. She ushers me into a small mudroom that is covered top to bottom in round blue circles that look similar to the eye-like pattern of a peacock feather. They are lined up in neat rows against a white painted wall and stare out from every direction. It isn't wallpaper, but actual amulets that have been attached to the wall. Hot glue, it looks like.

"Um, Ms. Rosalyn?" I ask, staring at the wall. "I don't mean to be rude, but what is all over your walls?"

"Hmm?" Ms. Rosalyn looks over from where she is hanging my coat in a small cutout closet. "Oh, yes, these are evil eyes. They're here to keep the evil spirits away."

"Ah, of course. I see," I say, not seeing it at all. I wonder what it will take to remove them.

"This way, Mr. Caddel," Ms. Rosalyn calls, shuffling out of the mudroom. I follow her, eyeing the evil eyes on my way out.

"This is the living room," she says, walking around the most eccentric living room I've ever seen. There's a paisley couch that looks like it's from the 1980s. Next to the couch, sitting on a side table is a golden ninja turtle lamp with a bright pink lampshade that has a feathered fringe, also in pink. An ornamental rug sits in the middle of the floor. There are a few chairs scattered around the rug, but they look old and uncomfortable. I have recently gone to a museum and there was an exhibit of renaissance chairs, and these look remarkably similar with their flat seats and ornate backings and arms. Along the top of the wall all around the room, there is a strip of wallpaper of an ornate sword dripping blood.

I stand in shock for a minute before turning to Ms. Rosalyn's expectant face.

"Well?" she asks.

I clear my throat and look around desperately for something to say. My eyes land on the rug and, noticing that the cracks between the floorboards leading under it look dark with the beginnings of water damage, I gesture to it.

"Do you mind if I look under it?" I ask.

"Of course not! Feel free," Ms. Rosalyn says, smiling widely.

I fold the rug over, looking for a stain or warping, and am surprised at what I do find.

"What is this?"

There is a clear square cut in the wood that looks like a trapdoor.

"Oh, that was a secret bunker during the 1860s for the civil war. That's around the time this house was built. You can open it if you'd like. There's nothing much down there," Ms. Rosalyn says.

I stare at her for a moment, and then at the trapdoor. Bracing myself, I dig my fingers into the crack and try to gain leverage. With some slight shifting, I manage to get one end up and lift the piece of flooring out of the way. As I peer down into the darkness a flashlight appears over my shoulder and shines into the darkness. I lean away and see that Ms. Rosalyn is holding the flashlight. I give her a smile of thanks and take it, looking down into the bunker. Ms. Rosalyn is right, there really isn't anything. Just some garbage in a corner, a smashed teacup, and... I shudder. There's a small pile of bones in one corner, glints of white reflecting from behind dirt and grime. I grab the piece of flooring hurriedly and put it back in place and throw the rug back over it.

"Uh... um, okay... how about the next room?" I say, standing up and brushing off the imaginary dust of bones.

"Yes, of course. This way," Ms. Rosalyn says, then takes me out into the hallway. The hallway is, much to my surprise, made completely of tile. The floors are tile. The walls are tile. Even the ceiling is somehow tile. I'm not sure how that was accomplished, and despite my admiration for the feat, it makes the hall look monotonous and never-ending.

"Is, uh..." I clear my throat and gesture to the tiles. "Is there a way to get to the wiring without completely destroying the walls?" I ask.

"Oh, I haven't the slightest idea," Ms. Rosalyn says, smiling blankly up at me. I at once feel a deep sympathy for the house.

"This is the guest bedroom," she says, bringing me through a door next to the living room. I look around and am glad to see that this room at least is relatively normal. Sure, there are definitely too many oil paintings of some old man with a curly white mustache and a foot-long beard, but other than that, pretty normal.

"Across the hall is the bathroom," Ms. Rosalyn directs, pointing to a door. It has a peace sign carved into it, scratched there by a knife. I swing the door open and jump when I hear a crash. I look behind the door and find that the door has hit the toilet. The toilet that is right next to the door. I shake my head slightly and grimace, because if somebody had been sitting there, the door knob would have struck them right in the head. The sink is shaped to look like a stone and has one of those waterfall spouts, and an old clawfoot tub takes up an entire wall.

"When was the last time you had your septic system checked?" I ask, turning on the faucet and watching the stream of water, checking the water color and flow strength. Ms. Rosalyn gives me a strange look.

"You get your septic system checked?" She laughs, small and quiet. "I don't think I even know where my septic system is!"

I stare at her in concern before plastering on a tight smile. I didn't think the house looked in too bad a shape, but Ms. Rosalyn apparently knows nothing about house upkeep, and this might turn into a big and expensive project. This most definitely is not the house that my wife and I are looking for.

Stepping back into the completely tiled hallway, I give Ms. Rosalyn a polite smile.

"Well, Ms. Rosalyn, it was nice to meet you, but I think I've seen enough. So, I'll-" I begin, trying to leave.

"Oh no, don't go yet!" she cries. "You still have to see the attic!"

"Alright," I concede. She looks so sad to see me go, and I don't have the nerve to make an old lady cry. "Just the attic, and then-"

"Just through here, Mr. Caddel," she interrupts, and walks through another door to the right of the bathroom.

Ms. Rosalyn, in fact, does not bring me to the attic but instead takes me into the kitchen so she can check on her meal. I'm not sure what she's cooking, but it smells delicious. The kitchen, unlike the rest of the house, is normal. Not even a little dirty. It is impeccably clean and with everything in its place. Even the inside of the microwave looks as clean as if it was brand new.

"Oh, and you'll stay for dinner, of course," Ms. Rosalyn remarks, leaving no room for argument. I open my mouth to protest, but a clock sounds from the next room, and Ms. Rosalyn looks up from peering into the oven. I look into what must be the dining room and see a grandfather clock chiming away in the corner.

"Oh, is that the time already?" Ms. Rosalyn says. "We'll have to hurry up the tour then. We wouldn't want to miss them."

"Them?" I ask in confusion but get no response. Ms. Rosalyn has already headed into the dining room, shuffling by in her black slippers.

"Come along, then," she calls in her whispery voice.

I call after her. "Who is 'them'? And why are we meeting with them?"

Ms. Rosalyn still doesn't respond. I don't even try to protest against staying again. Clearly, she is set on having me as a dinner guest, and I'm too much of a pushover to say no to a lonely old lady.

With a deep sigh, I follow Ms. Rosalyn into the next room. She gestures to a table standing at one end of the dining room.

On it stands a giant ball of metal strings all wrapped around and around. I take a step closer and realize that they're guitar strings.

"This ball is made up of all the guitar strings that my son broke or used until he died, bless his soul," Ms. Rosalyn says, dabbing at her eyes. "Sometimes, I like to think that he looks out and can see this trophy of his talent and ambition."

"I bet he loved you very much," I say, trying to be reassuring but doing an awkward job at it. But my smile dies when I see her look. A shiver goes down my spine.

"No, he doesn't. He goes to great lengths to tell me that all the time." Ms. Rosalyn's voice is still whispery, still soft, but there's a tone of foreboding underneath it, one that suggests knowing something one should not.

Then she points to the opposite wall and says, "That's Frouglas."

I turn and find that there is a hamster tunnel of chicken wire running along the wall, and within the maze of chicken wire and hay, a rooster is pecking indignantly at the ground and staring right at me with one eye.

"Don't worry, he's nice," Ms. Rosalyn assures.

"Sure," I mutter, as Frouglas stares me down while ferociously pecking at a carrot that's lying in the cage. "Nice." I don't even want to ask about the upkeep of the rooster cage. Or look at the floor underneath it.

"Right through here is the drawing room," Ms. Rosalyn says, already moving on to the next room through a door connected to the dining room. The drawing room has a huge, cracked tv on one wall; a fireplace that has blue fire flickering in it; and a billiard table in the middle. All the balls on the billiard table are neon, and one of them is flashing brightly. There are also stuffed animal heads lining the walls, and no chairs in sight, although there are multiple beanbags and cushions lying on the floor.

"And right across from the drawing room is the master bedroom. It has a full bathroom connected to it in the back," Ms.

Rosalyn dictates, leading me across the hall and into the master bedroom. Or at least what Ms. Rosalyn claims to be the master bedroom. It's completely empty except for a stuffed cat lying in the middle of the room.

"Ms. Rosalyn, why is there only a stuffed toy cat in the master bedroom?" I ask, staring at the threadbare toy cat who seems to be staring back.

"Oh, don't mind Whinnifer. He's always suspicious of newcomers. He'll get used to you in no time," Ms. Rosalyn laughs. "Right through that door is the master bathroom. It has a shower," she adds like it's the highlight of the entire house. And who knows, maybe it is. It's at least got to be the most normal thing in this house.

I take a step forward to look at the master bathroom, and then I stop. Something is... wrong. I feel dizzy and sick to my stomach. The world starts to tilt and swirl. The white walls of the bedroom bleed color splotches, dripping down across the walls. Ms. Rosalyn's voice snaps me out of it.

"Oh, Whinnifer, stop torturing the young man," Ms. Rosalyn scolds. The world switches back to normal like a breath that was stolen, and I take a step back, panting.

"What was that?" I ask, breathless.

"That was just Whinnifer. Like I said, he'll get used to you pretty quickly, but he doesn't like strangers."

"Ah, right. Of course, it's the stuffed cat- er, Whinnifer, sorry. Of course. Right, well..." I look at Ms. Rosalyn expectantly. "Are there any other rooms that I need to see?" I ask, avoiding looking at the apparently semi-sentient stuffed cat that lives in the master bedroom and hogs the shower.

"Just the basement and the attic. But we'll look at the attic after we eat. It's not time to see them quite yet," Ms. Rosalyn says. I open my mouth to ask about this 'them' she keeps mentioning, but she's already shuffled off, leaving me alone in the room with the cat. "This way to the basement!" she calls. I follow Ms. Rosalyn as quickly as I can.

Ms. Rosalyn guides me to the end of the hallway and to an open doorway with hanging beads working as a makeshift door between the hallway and the stairs, and that leads directly to a staircase. It's just one, long continuous staircase from the attic to the basement without bothering to stop at the main level. There are no turns or doubling back, just a straight up-and-down staircase. There's no landing to get to the stairs; you just have to step onto the staircase and pick a direction. I sigh at the ridiculousness of the house's architecture. Whoever designed it truly had a screw loose.

"Just down here," Ms. Rosalyn calls, heading down the stairs. I follow her, having to step up to get onto the staircase. "Now, I don't really utilize the basement; it's normally too much of a fuss for me to go up and down all the time."

I get to the basement and flip the glow-in-the-dark switch, revealing a few sputtering light bulbs that flicker to life. The only things that are here are spiderwebs and a handful of boxes. I lead the way up the staircase, past the beaded doorway, and up towards the attic, when Ms. Rosalyn lets out a cry.

"What, what is it?" I ask, hurrying back down to make sure she's okay. She grabs my shirt and pulls me close, breathing into my face.

"You do not-" she hisses- "go into the attic unless it is time..." She pants heavily for a moment before letting me go and pushing me out to the main level. "Come on, now, dinner is almost ready."

"Hold on a minute," I say, catching up to her in the hallway and gripping her arm. "Who is 'they' and why are you so scared of them?" I demand. Her eyes widen and she looks scared, so I let go and ask in a gentler tone, "Have they done anything to you? Have they hurt you? You can tell me if they've hurt you."

"Oh, no, it's nothing like that. That's very sweet of you to be worried, but really, you'll find out after dinner, I promise. But I think my timer is going off, and really, it's not time to see them yet anyways, and-" she prattles on and on, taking my arm and leading me to the dining room. I look over my shoulder at the hanging beads, still swinging slightly, but I let Ms. Rosalyn lead me away. She leaves me in the dining room and shuffles into the kitchen, getting dinner sorted. Frouglas is in a different part of his maze cage, staring at me with anger flecked eyes while pecking at a hamster ball. I'm not too sure what a hamster ball is doing in a rooster cage, but knowing what I do of Ms. Rosalyn, I'm not entirely surprised.

Ms. Rosalyn is humming in the kitchen accompanied by the clinking of plates as she cheerfully plates the food. My mind keeps going back to the 'them' and who 'they' could possibly be, and what they have to do with the attic. Pausing a moment to make sure that Ms. Rosalyn isn't about to come around the corner, I walk as quietly as I can out of the room and to the staircase.

I push through the beads that try to tangle around me. I notice that the staircase walls are covered in burn marks and scratches, marks that aren't on the walls down to the basement. The higher I climb, the colder the air gets. By the time I get to the top, I can see my breath. I reach for the doorknob and wince as I touch the frigid metal. Sucking in a breath, I grab the doorknob and throw it open as quickly as I can.

I step into the attic and find the ground covered in fog, swirling and burning cold to the touch. There are symbols drawn on the walls in black paint and the same scratches and burn marks from the stairway cover the walls. On the far side of the room, there's a large, circular window made of black glass that overlooks the backyard. Through the stained glass, I can just barely make out the shape of the full moon rising.

"Hello?" I call out, shivering hard and my breath all but crystalizing in the air in front of me. "Is anyone here?"

No answer. My legs start to blister and bleed where the fog has touched me. Alarm pools in my stomach, and a gargled sound of fear and pain comes out of my throat. I shift painfully from leg to leg, trying to minimize the pain, and look around one last time before leaving. I turn around and find Ms. Rosalyn standing in the doorway.

"You'll like it up here," she hums, eyes pitch black. "It is a shame that you weren't able to try my turkey biscuit skillet." Her smile stretches and she tilts her head slightly. "Now you'll join my son and all the others who tried to take my house from me."

The fog starts to move faster, swirling wildly through the air and burning me at every touch. Humanoid figures of smokey light appear around the attic, ghostly figures with no faces or features, simply silhouettes that stand frozen except for the turning of their heads. Ms. Rosalyn steps forward, and I take a step back. She starts to chant, black bile bubbling from her mouth as acidic words pour from her throat. Again, I am overcome with the sick dizziness that I felt in Whinnifer's room, that stomach roiling sickness. Eyes that look exactly like Frouglas's appear in the smoke, so many of them, floating around and around, watching me. I hear tiles shattering and the grandfather clock chiming. Ms. Rosalyn steps forward, her chanting accompanied by the shapes around me that fill the attic, and the fog consumes me, burning me away little by little. I stumble backward, screaming in pain, and continue to thrash and trip until I hit the black glass window. The fog pushes me against it, burning me, burning me. There's a deep, rumbling laugh that trembles throughout the attic, and then Ms. Rosalyn's face is in mine, pitch-black eyes pouring smoke, her bloody mouth open and laughing. She pushes me and I pass through the window and directly onto the lifted sword of a statue of King Arthur claiming Excalibur. The full moon glints off the immovable blade bathed in blood and continues to shine maliciously through the unbroken black attic window.

And that is the end of my life in a body. That is the end of a life that is normal. Because my body has been pushed through the black glass window - somehow not breaking it - but my soul was grabbed by Ms. Rosalyn. She forces my struggling soul to the center of the room, where the fog clears away from the floor, revealing splattered marks and symbols written in blood. She catches a handful of the bile that is spilling from her mouth, and using two fingers, draws symbols on my soul. Burning, acidic symbols that bind me to her attic.

Once the burning stops, and the fog calms down, and the bubbling bile stops dripping, and Frouglas's eyes pop away, and there is no more dizziness, noise, or chaos, Ms. Rosalyn leaves. I am left standing in a room of faded humanoid shapes, just barely there, trapped as an empty soul in the attic of a little old lady.

After Ms. Rosalyn leaves, the souls slowly fade into nothing, and I assume I do as well. My skin still burns where the fog touched me and where Ms. Rosalyn burned symbols onto me, tying me to her house and confining me to the attic. There's a gaping ache in my chest, and it feels like I was run through. I try to move. I can't. I can't talk either, and I can just barely think. This attic is connected to Ms. Rosalyn and the entire house, and now I am too, and so I'm swimming with the knowing and the pounding of the overwhelming details flooding from the house and the old lady. I know of every creak and whisper, every mote of dust and crack in the wall. So it's a wonder when I can make out the shuffling of Ms. Rosalyn's black slippers as she makes her way to the front door. The creaking of the door opening splits through me, and then, with a sense of dread that overwhelms my connection to everything in the house, I hear Ms. Rosalyn as she greets my wife.

EVERYBODY KNOWS...

by Lilah Gray
The Children's House, 8th Grade

I sit in the back of the class like I do every day. I avoid conversations and people. Sometimes I just sit and sleep, which would explain my terrible grades that were once so perfect. Every now and then, my teacher Mr. Jacobs, asks me about my grades and tells me he understands how I feel but that I need to bring them back up. When he tells me this, I just nod and walk away. I feel like I won't ever bring my dropping grades back up. I won't ever get my friends back. I won't ever have a life again, and at this point, I just don't care anymore. I wish nobody could know what had happened that terrible afternoon, but that's not the case. Everybody knows...

I had a perfect life, a solid friend group, a boyfriend, a best friend, perfect grades, a middle-class family, and everything was great. I would wake up every morning and get dressed; I always wore nice, freshly cleaned clothes, folded and neat. My parents would always compliment me, and friends always told me I should show off my body because it's perfect. My friends would constantly talk about how they wished they looked like me. I was the stereotypical blonde, blue-eyed, skinny girl you see in the movies. I knew I looked good. I would wear short skirts, crop tops, and ripped jeans. If they accentuated my body, then I would wear them. I was so confident, or at least that's what everyone thought. Nobody knew that I would wake up every morning, look in the mirror and judge everything about myself. I would do my makeup, enough to cover all the little imperfections on my skin, but not too much to make my face "cakey."

I then would make my way downstairs to grab an orange, say good morning to my parents, and I was on my way to school. I would hop on the bus, put on headphones, and get an extra 20 minutes of sleep. I would arrive at school and flip a switch in my brain. I became happy and social. I was no longer the girl who judged everything about herself. I was the confident girl who was perfect in every way. I didn't mind being that; it beats being made fun of; I was praised for my perfection. I would sit through all my classes, then after school, I would take the bus back home. I would change my clothes and put on shorts and a t-shirt. I would run about a mile, come home, shower, and finish my homework. Everyone thought my life was perfect, just like me.

I did not believe it at the time, but now I wish I could go back to those days when all I had to worry about was what I would wear the next day. None of this is the case anymore, not since that one day. I don›t wear makeup anymore, I stopped dressing up, and I would go to school in sweats and a hoodie every morning. Headphones on. This allows me to tune out the world around me. I started ignoring my friends, stopped doing and turning in my homework, and broke up with my boyfriend. I tried to continue my life as normal, but it was impossible; everything people said to me was a reminder of what had happened. The thing is, nobody ever really found out. It remains a mystery to all but two people in this world, my father and I, or at least that's what we thought.... Nobody else was truly supposed to know what happened that night.

Today felt different. I don't know why but it did. I had my usual routine. I got up quickly, changed, and walked out to wait for the bus. When I woke up, my father wasn't waiting for me in the kitchen; I assumed he just had to go to work early. I waited outside for the bus for about thirty minutes, but it was already 8:00. School had started, and I must have missed the bus. I decided I was not going to walk to school. I live about 15 miles away from the campus, so I decided to stay home. It's not like I was going to do anything at school anyway. I texted my dad to let him know that I missed the bus and that I would stay home. I never got a response.

I got a text from one of my old friends. It said:

Hey, did the bus pass your house today?
I thought I just missed the bus but Lexi
said it didn't come by her house either.

Usually, I ignored messages, but I chose to answer her this time.

I thought I missed it as well
-didn't stop by
maybe he overslept and forgot.
I don't mind, it means no school

She replied:

Hm... weird, I guess you're right
about the no school thing though
Nice to hear from you again
I miss you

I chose to ignore her after she said that. I am curious why the bus driver was late, but more than likely, he did actually oversleep.

I decided to ignore my nagging thoughts about the bus driver and make a sandwich. After eating my sandwich, I chose to go back to bed. I ended up sleeping till 8:30 PM.

I got up to see if my dad was home. When I walked into the kitchen, I saw him on the phone with somebody, probably someone he works with. I walk into the kitchen and say, "Hey, Dad."

He looks up and tells the person on the phone, "I've got to go, bye." And then he hangs up. "Hey, have you eaten dinner yet?" he asks.

"No, I've been asleep," I replied.

"Oh, okay, I'll make pasta."

The rest of the night was chill. We just ate dinner and went our separate ways.

When I woke up the next morning, I grabbed a piece of fruit and went to wait outside for the bus. But just like yesterday, it never came. I decided to text the same old friend who messaged me yesterday morning:

Did it come today?

To which she replied:

no, maybe he is just sick

I text back:

I guess so

I decided instead of going back inside, I was going to take a walk. I walked down to the neighborhood park and found a nice spot under a tree where I decided I would sit. I started thinking about the whole bus situation. Something did not seem right about the driver missing two days. They would have sent someone out in his place if he was sick. The more I miss school, the more absences I will rack up, which could prevent me from graduating. I have maintained a passing grade; I study for my tests, but my homework rarely gets done. I decided to email the school and see why the bus hasn't been coming.

Hello Mrs. Johnson,

I was just wondering why the bus driver has not picked me up for the last two days. I'm not able to get to school without the bus and I'm wondering if it will be back tomorrow?

Thanks,

Johanna Turnnum

I put my headphones on and sit quietly. As I look around, I see kids to the right of me playing at a playground while their moms sit on a nearby park bench and gossip while watching them. I see some teenagers walking their dogs. I see some older folks just taking a nice short stroll. I see one young woman who looks to be in her mid-twenties. When I make eye contact with her, she immediately looks away. I could tell she was staring at me. I've become used to it over the last few months. I continue to stare at her, so she knows that I saw her hoping that she won't look back. She doesn't, and she begins walking away. I successfully made her go away. As she leaves, I see a child run in front of her, and it causes her to almost fall on top of him. She saved herself before she did, but when she tripped, part of her hair moved to reveal blonde hair. She quickly fixed it and looked around to see if anyone noticed.

I looked away quickly. I recognized the woman in that instant. She was there the night that it happened. I saw her behind the police tape. I don't know why she was wearing a wig, but I also don't care. I start to make my way back home. When I do, I realize how long I spent at the park; it felt like mere minutes but was actually a few hours. As I walked, I saw the sun beginning to set. I love sunsets much more than sunrises. I find them more beautiful, and they give me closure. When I got home, my dad was making dinner. I walked into the kitchen and said, "Hi Dad, what's for dinner tonight?"

He replied, "I'm making tomato soup."

"My favorite," I responded. I then walked over to the living room and sat on the couch. We don't eat at the table anymore. My phone pinged. It was an email back from my principal.

Hello Ms. Turnnum,

We are currently unclear why your bus driver has not stopped by recently, but we are trying to figure it out. We will be sending a replacement for him tomorrow. Sorry for any inconvenience this issue may have caused.

Sincerely,

Mrs. Johnson

Well, sadly, my days of no school have come to an end, but it's for the best. I do wonder what happened to him. He was mean anyway. Always made snarky remarks about the kids on our bus, some of whom deserve them but many others who don't. I will gladly take a new guy. Just then, my dad came in with dinner. Dinner was good. We watched tonight's episode of Jeopardy, something my dad, mom, and I used to do all the time when I was younger. Now just my dad and I do it. It was almost nine. I decided I would just go to bed; I was very tired for some reason.

I woke up that night at around two a.m. I had a dream about the woman I caught staring at me in the park. She was lighting my house on fire and just watching me as I helplessly burned alive inside. I'm not surprised that the dream woke me up. I guess our interaction freaked me out a little bit. I eventually fell back to sleep, knowing that in a few hours, I would have to deal with my Spanish teacher yelling at me in my first-period class because I missed school. Not that it was my fault. She's never been the most sympathetic teacher. When the incident first happened, everyone was so kind. Not her; she didn't care. All she wanted was for me to turn in my homework. I slept fine for the remainder of the night.

When I awoke later that morning, I threw on my favorite hoodie and jeans and was off. The bus was almost to my house when I walked outside. I quickly got on. We had a different bus driver, which was no surprise to me. It was a woman this time. She was old but said good morning to me when I climbed the steps. I walked to the back of the bus and took my usual seat. On went, the headphones, and I enjoyed my extra bit of sleep.

Today was the same as every other day at school, although everyone seemed a little on edge. I wonder why. I know we have finals coming up soon, but I guess it makes sense. I have to start studying. I don't have to do great. I just need a passing grade. After what happened, I chose to reject all of the colleges I applied to and stay at home with my dad. He was okay with that, and nobody blamed me.

After school, I got home and found Dad sitting on the couch about to watch a basketball game. I waved and walked into my room. I choose to study for a few hours. I tired of studying around 5:30 and decided to watch the news because I knew Jeopardy would follow. I watched the usual weather, then just boring stuff about the world and our local community. I wasn't paying much attention; I was just sitting on my phone on Instagram. That is until I heard the reporter mention someone was missing.

My dad left the dinner he was cooking and walked into the living room. "Turn it up," he said.

"Local resident was reported missing early Wednesday morning. His employers were sent to his house late Tuesday night, and when nobody answered, police were notified. Police declared that nobody had been seen in that house for at least twenty-four hours. This person remains a mystery to all. His name was searched in the database of town residents, and there have been no reports of anybody with that name. More information will hopefully come soon. And that's the news for this Thursday night."

I looked at my father's worried face. I asked him, "Why do you look scared?"

"Oh um- I - I just feel bad for his family," he stuttered.

I nodded. "Do you want to watch Jeopardy with me now?

"I am not feeling it tonight. Maybe tomorrow?" He asked.

"Sure, Dad," I responded.

The next day at school, everyone talked about what we had heard on the news last night. Nobody knows who is missing. Not much happens in this town, so things spread fast, but this went through really fast. When I walk past people, they stare at me accusingly. I know I dealt with my things, too, but I have nothing to do with this. I got so annoyed that I stood up in the middle of my history class and said, "I have nothing to do with this missing person so go find somebody else to stare at and leave me alone." That did not help at all. Now they were also starring during my little outburst. I got detention for interrupting the class and for being disrespectful. My dad had to work late today, so I walked to a nearby beach and waited till he could pick me up. He didn't arrive until 9:00. When I got in the car, my dad asked what had happened. I told him that a bunch of kids kept looking at me after they heard about the story on the news last night, and I got mad and yelled at them in class and ended up with detention.

He did not seem mad; he just told me, "you can't do that again; you're bringing too much attention to yourself, and that's just going to make it worse." I nodded, and we drove the rest of the way home in silence. When we got home, my dad offered to make food for me, but I told him "no" and went to bed.

I had to go upstate over that weekend to finalize some things related to my mom. I missed school on Monday. I apparently missed a lot. When I got to school, everyone was talking about one thing and one thing only. The body. A man's body had been discovered in a small lake nearby late Sunday night. It was later confirmed to be the body of the man we used to call our bus driver. Apparently, our bus driver had been hiding his real name from everyone in town. When the school went to check up on him at his house, and he wasn't there, they discovered the name he had given didn't match anyone in town. Nobody knows why he chose to fake his identity, but he must have had a reason because he was more than likely killed over it. He was found with burn marks around his neck and a gash through his stomach. It has been ruled a murder. Someone in this town is a murderer. The question is, who? The rumors were so awful that the school called everybody into the gym to talk about what had been happening. They said the same thing everyone already knew, who he was (or who we thought he was), how he died and worked here. They told us anyone who is caught bringing this up around classmates or teachers would have to report to the principal. The principal then started playing a video about trauma and how to get help. As she played it, I got a text message. It was from an unknown number.

I know what your father is hiding

I saw that, and I panicked. This person had to be trying to trick me. Nobody else knew but my father and I. Nobody...

When the video ended, I quickly got up and began to walk out. As I was leaving, I noticed a woman I did not recognize as a teacher or staff member. She had red hair. Not ginger-colored, but the fake kind you buy in a box at the store. I recognized her face. That's when it hit me; she had the same face as the blonde woman that had been staring at me when I was at the park. She was quickly walking out of the gym. I asked a random kid next to me if she worked here. He just shrugged and walked away. The woman I thought she was, is blonde, though this person has red hair. It could be her. She has worn a wig before. Who's to say she's not wearing one again? If it is her, though, then why is she at my school? She doesn't work here and is much too old to be a student. I ran to try and catch her. I made it out to the parking lot and saw her get in her car. She quickly pulled away. As she took off her wig to reveal the blonde hair, I knew she had. I don't know who this woman is or what she is doing, but she is everywhere I go. I'm sure it's just a coincidence.

Our bus ride home was almost silent. When I got home, I decided to walk to that park again. When I got there, it was almost empty. Just a child and her mom playing together at the park. The child laughed as her mom pushed her on the swing, just like my mother used to do for me. I took a seat on a bench and just thought over all the events that had happened over the course of the last 7 hours. I found out my bus driver was murdered, I saw the same person that was at the park last time I was here, and someone else might know something about that night. I sat there and thought about this all until I eventually fell asleep.

When I woke up, it was two in the morning. I was still on the park bench. I looked at the time and was flooded with texts and calls from my dad asking where I was and threatening to call the cops. I called him to let him know I was okay; I didn't get an answer, so I sent him a text.

Hey dad, sorry I fell asleep at the park,
on my way home now sorry for worrying you I'm okay

When I got home, he was waiting right at the door, absolutely furious with me. He started yelling.

"Dad, I have to tell you something," I said. He ignored me and continued. I repeated myself this time much louder. "Dad, I have to tell you something."

He stopped and said, " I don't want to hear–"

I cut him off before he could finish his sentence. "Somebody might know...." I said.

He went silent. "Who and how?" he calmly asked.

"I don't know the answer to either of those questions." With that, he walked into his room and shut the door. I did the same.

My dad called me in sick for the remainder of the week. He monitored my phone and would not let me leave the house. He was very paranoid that someone did actually know the secret. At first, I thought it was a prank, but then I received a letter in the mail. It was a small piece of paper with "I know how she died" written. No return address. I did not show it to my father. I wanted to leave this house again, and secrets were the only way I could do that. Later that night, I snuck out for a breath of fresh air. As I sat on the steps, I noticed someone walk past me. It was the blonde. I debated going up to her, and eventually, I just decided to do it. I walked up behind her and tapped her on the shoulder. She ignored me and continued walking. I tapped again, but she still ignored me. This time I sternly said "stop," and she did. She turned and faced me. When she turned, I realized it was not the woman I thought it was, she was blonde, but the faces did not match. I am surprised by her not being who I thought she was.

I turn around and just start running. I ran back inside and shut the door. I sat on the couch for the remainder of the night and eventually fell asleep. The blonde woman I've been recognizing and the one I thought I recognized were in my dreams, standing next to each other, just watching me. When I woke up the next morning, nobody was home. My dad, I guess, had left the house for the first time in a week, and I chose to use that to my advantage. I walked over to the local grocery store and bought some food. We hadn't been shopping in days. I regretted my decision because then I had to walk all the way home with a bunch of groceries. When I got home, I walked inside and began to put away the groceries. I turned to go sit in the living room, and when I did, I stopped. There was a big red slash of something that looked like blood across our wall. I just stood there, confused. All of a sudden,

I heard the back door slam. I quickly ran in, but by the time I was there, the person or thing was gone. I called my dad but never got an answer. I decided I needed to call the police. I called and told them what had happened.

Someone broke into my house, painted a big slash with something resembling blood on my wall, and then they ran out. They showed up and analyzed the blood substance. My father was called, but still no answer. They told me to stay inside, lock all the doors and try and get a hold of my dad. They would send the results of the test back to me when they figured out what the blood-like thing was. My dad did not come home until late that night, almost 10:00 PM. I never heard back from him at all that morning. When I told him what had happened, he looked terrified. Not when he found out about the break-in but when he heard that I had called the police. He looked angry and scared and got mad because the police came to the house.

"You didn't answer the phone, and I did what I had to do," I told him. He paused and stared at me, then walked away and went into his room.

I went to school the rest of the week. Nothing else strange happened. It was a normal few weeks, and as the end of May grew closer, everyone was restless to finish off the school year. It wasn't until one day in mid-May that my world blew up. We were sitting through an assembly for mental health awareness month, and the principal was playing a video about suicide and the warning signs. We all sat there watching it. All of a sudden, it cut out for a second. When it came back on, it wasn't the video we had been watching. It was a video of the blonde girl. She said, "we all know the young girl who goes by the name of Johanna." People turned and faced me. "We all know about the tragic death of her mother. What we do not know is what actually happened that night. Her mother did not commit suicide. Her mother was murdered, and I don't know who did it, but I will find out. This is a message to Johanna, watch your back cuz pretty soon your world will crash harder than you ever thought it could." With that, the video cut out. The room was silent. I quickly ran out of that gym. I ran as fast and as far as I could towards my house. I called my dad, and he answered. I told him where I was and that I needed him ASAP.

"What happened," he asked when he got to me.

"Somebody knows that mom was murdered. The entire school knows now too!"

My dad gasped and then just started driving. He drove to our house, and we went inside. He quickly put a bunch of clothes in a suitcase. I asked where he was going. He told me, "I have to leave, or else it will be bad. Take the money, and if anyone asks, I'm on a work trip. If police come, say that you won't talk unless a lawyer is present. I love you." He put money on the counter, and then he walked out and sped away.

Within the hour, police showed up to question me about what had happened at school. I told them exactly what I was supposed to say. "I will not talk without a lawyer present." Eventually, they gave up trying to talk and told me they would be back. My phone was blowing up with texts from people at my school and emails from my teachers. I did not go to school and refused to show my face in public. The police did come back, but I told them the same thing every time.

After two weeks of living by myself and not leaving the house, I saw a car pull up. It was my father. When he walked inside, I instantly hugged him. We sat down, and I asked if he was able to come home.

He said, "in a way." I was just happy to have him home. I didn't even question what that meant. He told me he was tired and wanted to get some sleep, so we both went to bed. Later that night, I was awoken by flashing lights outside my window. I walked outside to see four cop cars. There were seven cops, all pointing guns at me. I immediately put my hands up. One officer yelled at me to get down on the ground. I did as I was told. A cop handcuffed me and moved me over to the grass. He then asked where my father was. I told him I didn't know. The rest of the cops moved inside. After ten minutes, I saw my father walk outside with a cop on either arm, handcuffed.

"You're under arrest for the murder of Charlotte Turnnum and James Beckham. Anything you say can and will be used against you in the court of law," they said as they put him in the squad car and drove away with my father. I was too stunned to speak. The police officer who handcuffed me put me into his vehicle, and we followed. As we drove away, I saw my neighbors on their lawns with a look of shock on their faces.

When we reached the police station, they brought me into a room to interrogate me. I told them exactly what I was told to tell the police if this ever happened. "I thought my mom committed suicide. My mom and dad loved each other there is no way he could have ever killed her, no possible way." After a few hours of questioning, I was released to a social worker. I was placed temporarily in a foster home. I wasn't allowed my phone; it was taken by police as evidence. It was not for a week until I heard the news about my father through my social worker. His preliminary hearing was tomorrow, and he was planning on pleading innocent.

The morning of his final day in court, I showed up at the courthouse. His trial began, and when it came time for his plea, he turned to face me for a moment.

My father mouthed the words *I love you*, turned and faced the judge, then said something I will never forget. "I plead guilty to both charges."

Everyone on the jury gasped. I sat with my jaw wide open, absolutely shocked. After a moment, I stood up and said, "Dad, what are you doing?" My social worker told me I needed to sit down, but I refused and started telling him that he was innocent. My social worker had to pull me out of the courthouse.

Within an hour, I found out my father's sentence. When I heard it, I broke down in tears. Life imprisonment without parole. That day my father was moved to prison. I was a month away from 18, and until my birthday, I was to stay with my foster family. After a few weeks, I was pulled into the police station one final time. They asked me what motivated my father to commit these murders. I lied and said I didn't know the answer. Eventually, I adjusted to the fact that I would never get a hug from my father again, that I would never watch Jeopardy with him, and that I would never get to feel his touch again.

Six months later

When I turned 18, I immediately moved out of my town; the memories were too painful, and I couldn't go anywhere without being questioned. It took a few months for me to paste together the whole truth. I knew my father had killed my mother, and I knew why. She had been using him for money, and he knew it, but when he found out she was cheating on him, he got mad. Very mad. I was angry, too; she had ruined my life. My father threw a glass, hitting her head, and when it broke, it cut her, and she ended up bleeding out. I was never a huge fan of my mom, but I couldn't believe what had happened.

My father made me promise not to ever tell a soul or something bad would happen. It turns out that he killed my bus driver because he had been trying to figure out who murdered her. Apparently, he and the blonde lady were working together. My mother and the bus driver had been having an affair, which sparked the bus driver's interest in figuring out what had happened. They had figured out it was my father, and when he got the tip that my bus driver knew, my father did what he had to do and killed him. I didn't know any of this information until I was able to speak to him. As I look back at it, I remember seeing my mother leave late at night, saying she got called into work late.

My dad ended up pleading guilty so that I would not go down with him. He knew he couldn't keep it a secret forever. I never figured out who the blonde lady was, and I doubt I ever will. I haven't seen her since that day. I visit my father in prison once a month, and he's always happy to see me. I think he's happy he doesn't have to live in constant fear of being caught anymore.

I will always wish that he had chosen innocence. If he had, I would still have a dad. But he made his decision, so I could live my life. The only thing that makes it hard for me to do is knowing that what happened, who my father was, who I am, and what he did is all public, and now... everybody knows.

MURDER ME TICKLED
by Kristen May
Traverse City Central High School, 10th Grade

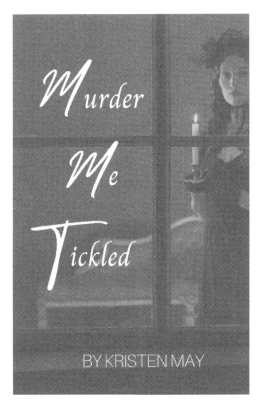

Chapter 1

It is October 27, 1854. When I wake up, the air is freezing outside my blankets. The birds are screeching, and I groan as I bury my head under the covers, willing myself to go back to a peaceful, dreamless sleep.

"Miss, it's time to get up. Your father is waiting for you in the dining hall," my butler, Gerald, says softly from my doorway.

"No," I mumble, pulling the covers further over my head. "It's too cold to get out of bed." I peek my eyes out from under the covers and give him my most charming smile. It must need work because he simply stares at me until I swing my legs over the bed. I usher Gerald out of my room and tell him to please get Anna for me. As I wait, I curl up in my window seat and peer outside. I see our groundskeeper, Henry, picking up the one or two leaves that are left on our otherwise spotless grounds. I'll bet all of my savings he's whistling.

"Hello, Henry!"

"Why hello Miss Phaedra! How are you this fine morning?"

"Well, I don't know if I would call it a fine morning. I'm freezing my buttocks off up here!" "The cold air is simply Mother Nature reminding us to better appreciate the warm weather, Miss!" Henry smiles with all his teeth and then returns to his task. I never understand how Henry is always so positive. Sometimes it seems like he's too positive. Like he's trying to cover something up by always being so cheerful. But then I banish those thoughts because if I started being suspicious of everyone who has strange quirks, there'd be nobody in my life I would trust. Even when all appears hopeless, he wears a crooked grin on his face and reminds us to think good thoughts. I figure it's a curse, really, to always find pleasure in things.

"Phaedra, may I come in?"

I grin as I recognize the voice, hopping off the window seat and crossing the room to sit on my bed. Anna is the only one who's allowed to call me Phaedra with no formalities, except for my father of course. She's been my maid and best friend since I was a wee babe. Now, eighteen years later, she knows me better than my own father does. *Not that that's saying much*, I think bitterly. "Phaedra?"

"Yes, Anna. Please come in."

She bustles in and gapes at me.

"Phaedra, look at yourself! Your hair is in disarray and your clothing is all rumpled! You do know that your father is waiting for you?" Anna reprimands me, hands on her petite hips.

"How would I remind my father how lucky he is to have me in his presence if I don't occasionally make him wait?" I say sweetly.

She just looks at me and shakes her head. "Come here, Phaedra. We must get you dressed before your father throws a fit. You know how he gets in the morning," Anna murmurs.

"Do I?" I pout and pretend to think, finger on my chin. "You know, I don't recall hearing anything about these so-called *fits*."

Anna beckons me with a flick of her finger. Sighing, I walk toward her and let her pull the dress over my head and settle it around my waist. I suck in a breath as she reaches behind me to tie the back. "You know, I really don't understand why I can't just wear trousers. They're so much easier to move in, and I can do high kicks in them. In these dresses, I can't even kick a man in the privates. How am I supposed to escape from one's clutches if I can't reach the privates?" I scowl and pick at the frivolous bows that pepper the dress. I hear light laughing behind me and crane my neck to see Anna chuckling. I close my eyes and let the sound soak into my mind. Her laugh is one that rivals the twinkling bells of the carriages. I let her carry on for about five more seconds before glaring at her. "It's not funny, Anna! You never know what trouble I might get in. I've been told that I'm quite the pest." I scowl and continue picking at my dress, taking my frustration out on the lace and ribbons. She swats my hand away before stepping back to survey her work.

"It's not perfect but it will have to do." She nearly shoves me out the door. "Go, go! You don't want to anger your father any more than he undoubtedly already is."

I nearly trip over all the ridiculous layers of my dress and when I glance back to shoot Anna a dirty look, I find that she has already exited the room and is hurrying down the hall. I frown, puzzled that she's in such a hurry, but I'm directed back to the task at hand when my hand brushes the ribbon on my dress, and I'm reminded once again, why I'm stuck in a ridiculous dress standing in the middle of the hall. I feel an urge to plop down in the middle of the overly decorated hallway (I mean seriously, how many paintings of flying babies does one person really need?) and pout, but there are passing servants, and if I've learned one thing in my lifetime it's that news, or should I say gossip, moves really fast through the inner workings of the staff. If my father hears of me acting so petulant I'll get a scolding that will leave my ears ringing. With an aggressive dusting of my dress, I set off for the dining hall. I stride down the torch-lit hallways, trying to maintain an air of dignity and grace. (I'm pretty sure I didn't pull it off as I tripped several times and had to steady myself on one of the portraits of a flying baby.) Finally, I arrived at the dining hall, panting and more than a little sweaty.

"Crumpets," I mutter, trying to wipe off the beads of sweat that have appeared on my brow and back of my neck.

"Here you are, Miss." I hear a deep, gravelly voice behind me and whirl around. A tall, wiry, silver-haired man looks down at me, holding out a handkerchief.

"Oh, thank you," I say softly, hastily accepting the cloth and blotting at my skin. After doing all that I can I wave the handkerchief around, looking for a place to put it.

"Please Miss, allow me." He takes the handkerchief out of my hand and stores it in his breast pocket.

Now, don't get me wrong. I'm appreciative of the man for offering me the handkerchief, and I'm not trying to act ungrateful. However, nobody takes anything from me without my permission. I mean honestly. It's basic etiquette. I slit my eyes at him and take a step back, sizing him up. "What's your name?"

"Wyatt, Miss."

"Uh-huh. And do you work for my father?"

"Yes, Miss. I was hired only a little while ago."

"Is this your first time working in an environment like this?"

"Miss, I would love to continue this conversation, but isn't your father waiting for you?" Wyatt waves a hand toward the sealed, oak doors. I purse my lips, thinking.

"Why yes, I suppose he is." I pivot slowly until my back is to the new servant.

"Thank you for your help, good sir." I throw one last look back at him and survey him up and down. "And do throw away that handkerchief. I believe I see a sweat stain forming."

Chapter 2

I hold my breath as I open the door. Although the dining hall is ornately decorated, my attention is immediately drawn to my father. Stooped and gray, my father is hunched over his breakfast. However, despite his age, my father still has an aura that demands attention.

"Hello, father," I call softly. My voice echoes around the room, but my father does not look up. I look around and find to my surprise that the room is entirely empty, other than my father and me. My heart speeds up and my mouth pulls into a frown. Something is wrong, and as I approach my father's seat the hairs on the back of my neck rise. My stride increases until I'm nearly running and as I near his seat I stumble. I gasp. Drop to my knees. Crawl the rest of the way until my father's body is right above me. Now. Now I see the gash that has nearly sliced my father's body in half. You would think there would be blood but it's surprisingly clean as if his body has been wiped clean or... drained. There are spots of blood on the floor and what I pray isn't a piece of flesh. Tears spring to my eyes and drip down my face onto the floor, mixing with the blood. I hear. I hear a sound behind me. I turn. I see a painting. The last thing I see before darkness washes my mind is a baby's face, smiling wide. Laughing. *What a poor way to go,* I think as my body hits the floor.

Chapter 3

Light comes pouring in as my eyes are pried open. I grunt and yank my head to the side and close my eyes once more. All I want to do is go back to sleep. A rough, meaty hand grips my chin and forces it back to center.

'No," I groan, weakly straining against the fingers.

"Why isn't the medicine knocking her out?" I faintly hear voices in the distance. Medicine? What medicine? Am I drugged? Where am I? Let me out of here!

"Now now Missie, don't be making a fuss." Rancid breath washes over me and a gritty beard rubs against my face.

"If you didn't want me 'making a fuss' as you so delicately put it, then let me go at once! Do you know who I am? I mean, I don't want to pull rank, but let's be honest. I'm obviously better than you so just let. Me. Go." I try to make my voice strong, but I can't help the break that occurs when I think of the situation I'm in. My father has just died, nay, been *murdered*. I've been hit over the head with a painting of a *baby* for god's sake, and now I'm tied to something with a smelly man standing over me. Honestly! Does the world have a grudge against me or something?

"You're better than me? Ha! Please. Little lady, you have quite a tongue on you. Perhaps we should cut it off." The man stalks closer and draws a blade from some hidden place. As it's released from the scabbard it makes a sharp, screeching sound and I'm reminded of the calls of the birds that wake me up in the morning. Oh, how I wish it was them now.

"But if you cut off my tongue, how will the world enjoy my wonderful jokes and sarcasm?" I squeeze my lips together and make my eyes go wide.

"What kind of monster are you? Stop baiting, Phaedra." A familiar voice floats its way over to me. "Didn't your father teach you better than that? Where are your manners?" Ringing bells jingle in the air and I'm momentarily confused. Why is there a carriage down here? My mind won't accept it until I see the familiar shape. The shape of a maid. The shape of a friend. The shape of a sister. "Hello, Phaedra," Anna whispers, a smirk playing across her rosebud lips.

Chapter 4

"A-Anna?" I stumble over my words. I can't accept it. I won't accept it. No. No, I won't. It can't be Anna. Not the Anna that has dressed me and bathed me since I was young. Not Anna who has played with me and who has spent hours talking with me when my father was caught up in meetings or was found thoroughly intoxicated. Not Anna. Anna. Anna. Yet here she is, standing right in front of me. I can smell the jasmine perfume that she wears every day. It wafts up my nose and I breathe in gallons of it, trying to find any reason to believe that this isn't Anna. But there is no mistake. And so I compose myself and paste on a sickly sweet smile. A smile that's tinged with sorrow.

"Hello, Anna," I say, my voice slightly garbled. "Little bit musty down here, ain't it? Heard that isn't very good for the pores. Clogs em' right up!" I'm not sure when my brain shifted into automated mode but now I'm just running on pure adrenaline. "Perhaps we should go somewhere nicer? Ohh, I've heard that Nissa Park is a wonderful spot for a picnic. Let's go there. Yes, le-"

"Shut up," she says. I cringe inwardly but keep a straight face. "I'll cut straight to the chase. Why was your father killed?"

"Why are you asking me? I walk into the dining hall, see my father nearly sliced in half, and then I'm hit over the head with a portrait of a baby. Which was terribly rude!" I send daggers at the man who threatened to cut off my tongue. Oh, how the world would suffer if my tongue was cut off.

"Nobody here hit you over the head with a baby, Phaedra. Wyatt here was the one who found you and brought you here. We simply tied you up because you were thrashing around too much to be controlled." Anna circles around me like a shark circling its prey.

"Wyatt? But Wyatt is the tall, silver-haired man who gave me a handkerchief before I went to meet my father. *You're* not Wyatt. He is," I slur. Interestingly enough, Anna has gone very still and very white. She strides forward until we're nose to nose.

"A man named Wyatt gave you a handkerchief?" She breathes, and I can't help but think that her breath smells like peppermint. She whirls around until she's facing the stocky man and murmurs something in his ear.

"Hey! What are you folks talking about? I'm here too, you know. You want to include me in the conversation?" I giggle as they both turn to face me, their faces leached of color. "Why do y'all look so worried? There's nothing to be worried about. Be happy!" I sing. Not ten seconds later I find myself feeling quite sick. "Umm, I...I don't feel so w-" And I vomit all over myself. "How gross is that," I mutter and then the world fades once again.

Chapter 5

"Come closer, darling." My father beckons me to his side and bends down so we're face to face. He reaches out and taps the vine that wraps itself up and around my ear.

"Do you know what this is?" He whispers, his breath hot on my face. I didn't realize it at the time, but I've come to learn that that sickly sweet smell is a sure sign he's been drinking. "It's an earring, Daddy."

"Very good. And that earring is a family heirloom that has been passed down for generations. So I need you to remember how important it is, alright baby girl?"

"Yes, Daddy!" I smile and run my fingers up the vine, feeling every bump and crevice. This vine is a sure sign that my father trusts and loves me. I just know it.

Looking back, I sigh at my younger self, disappointed in my lack of good judgment. Oh, how naive I was to think that my father cared. How naive I was to think he would ever be the father of my expectations.

Chapter 6

"Hut, hut, hut, hut." I wake up to the rhythmic pounding of voices and find myself swaying side to side.

"What the - put me down right now!" I struggle against my ropes, but all I succeed in doing is rubbing my wrists raw. I fall limp and wonder what horrors await me now. Apparently, the horror is a well-dressed girl with ruby red lips and jasmine perfume. "Hello again, Anna." I tilt my head and smile at her pleasantly, despite the rage that boils beneath my skin.

Anna ignores me and looks to one of the men shrouded in black standing to my side. "Did you call the doctor?"

"Yes, ma'am. The appointment is all set and ready for."

"Good. Take her there now and see to it that he injects her."

"Right away, ma'am."

Anna strides away, her ruby lipstick the only thing I see before she descends into the shadows. "Ey, you." One of the goons (let's just call them goons for the time being) strides over to me and jerks my head up.

"Eh, what? Didn't your mother teach you any manners? You never touch a lady without her permission." I struggle against his meaty hand but all that achieves is a tighter grip. I mean honestly! What have I done to deserve this type of treatment?

"Now, now, now, none of that. You wouldn't want me to hurt you, would you?"

"Uh, of course not! What kind of idiot wants to be hurt? What I would *like* is to be released so I can forget all about this day!" I glare at him but he doesn't blink until I have to blink because my eyeballs are burning, which makes my glare entirely ineffective.

"This one's feisty, ain't she?" He roughly chucks me under the chin and chuckles, his laugh grating against my skin. As he goes to withdraw his hand, I bite him, sinking my teeth into his sweaty flesh. Ew, ew, ew, ew, ew!

"What the bloody hel- she bit me!" He jerks his hand away and rubs at the two bloody imprints that I've left on his forearm. His eyes flash up, burning with a thousand fires.

"Why, you little-!"

"What is going on in *here*?" A new, cool voice floats down the hallway and soaks into my ears. The goon straightens immediately and flashes a hand up to his forehead in a hurried salute. *Hmm*, I wonder, *who is this man and why does he command such an air of respect?*

"Why isn't she in my lab? Anna sent me up here to check and see if everything was all right. So I'll ask one more time. Why. Isn't. She. In. My. Lab?" He never raises his voice but his freezing tone sends shivers down my spine.

"I'm sorry, sir! She was causing a bit of trouble and we were just trying to resolve the issue." He swings his head around to look down his nose at me but I ignore him. Why does this new voice sound so familiar? If only I could see his face, but there are merely bits and pieces that are visible, and I can't connect them so they make sense. I feel like I hear it every day but it's not connecting. The man comes closer and I can hear his boots clicking on the floor.

"Hello, Phaedra," he purrs, his voice like a snake.

"Do I know you? I feel a little behind if we're already on a first-name basis." I respond, my voice a slow drawl. He barks a laugh and drifts a few feet closer.

"Oh, Phaedra, how I missed your ferocious little attitude. Honestly, it brings me back." The man inhales deeply as if the smell of me brings back memories.

"Unless the smell of armpit sweat and ranky breath brings back memories, I'm not sure what you're trying to accomplish by sniffing." He smiles.

"Phaedra, sweet, innocent Phaedra. You never knew did you? All of those days when you peered out of your window and called hello to me. When I was so damn cheerful. You never knew, did you?" I struggle to process the spew of words that are being thrown my way. He leans closer, shadows and light playing across his face. I tilt my head forward, as far as it can go, and stare into his black eyes. "Come closer," I breathe. He chuckles and shakes his head, turning around and moving back into the shadows. "Closer!" I snarl, spit flying as my lips peel back to expose my teeth. He halts and bends his head toward his chest. I wait, panting. But all he does is chuckle again. Chuckle. He *chuckles*. My father just died and he *laughs* at me. I want to rip free of my binds and launch myself at him, tearing and clawing until he's nothing more. As if he can read my thoughts, he turns slightly, his midnight eyes gleaming in the ray of light.

"Don't misbehave, Phaedra. Trust me, you don't want me to have to... calm you. I've heard that my method brings along interesting dreams." With those parting words of wisdom, he melts into the darkness.

Chapter 7

Not long after the mystery man leaves, I'm hefted up and thrust into the darkness after him. The shadows cloud my senses and leave me feeling disoriented and confused. Finally, I'm plopped down in the midst of a midnight sky. I struggle against the ropes in vain, worsening the abrasions that I already have on my wrists until I feel blood leak down my hands. I stop and think for a moment. How am I going to get out of this? As I'm pondering life's essential question, I hear a *thunk* from behind me. I jerk my head around.

"What the hell- " I'm cut off as a rug is jerked around my head and I'm yanked backward. My head collides with the floor and I immediately see spots.

"What are you doing?! Her head can't feel any impact for at least twenty-four hours! It alters the results!"

"Sorry, sir! It was an accident. Please forgive me, sir. Please have mercy."

"Oh, so I'm supposed to forgive you, am I? Your personal connection to her is jeopardizing everything! Perhaps it'd be better if you weren't a part of this anymore..."

"No, sir, please! Si-" *Shing.* The last thing I see before I fade once more into darkness is the head of a young woman, a pool of blood collecting underneath it. A woman that I know well. Anna?

...

I wake up to a scaly tail brushing across my face.

"No, five more minutes. Gerald..." *Squeak squeak!* I bolt upright, the rat going flying from my forehead. I gape, horrified at the prospect that this disgusting creature was on my face. I groan, rubbing my hand over my face. It's only when my hand comes away speckled with brown that I realize the rat must have... released bodily functions on me. I glare at the offending creature, wanting nothing more than to unleash all of my fury on this rodent. But as I advance on the rat, preparing to swing my raging fists at it, my emotions overcome me and I deflate, my body curling inward. Anna. Anna. *Anna.* My body racks with heaves, so sincere it hurts. However, there are no tears. No wetness pouring down my face, no droplets splattering on the rust-ridden floor. Nothing. My dry heaves subside, leaving me feeling empty and cold. Oh, so cold. My body operating on its own accord now, I bring myself to the corner of the cell, curling up in a ball, trying to protect myself from the outside horrors that now seem to control my life.

I'm jolted awake by the screeching of the cell door opening. A stocky man fills the opening and flicks one finger toward me. I blink at him, my brain too overwhelmed by the last few days to comprehend his meaning. He waits grumpily, becoming more and more irritated, until he groans, reaching to his belt and unsheathing a dagger. When he gestures to me with that blade, I understand immediately and groggily climb to my feet, wobbling unsteadily to the doorway. The stud man grabs me roughly and yanks me behind him down the dimly lighted hallway. We pass so many rooms with the same dirty cot and blank walls they all blur together. He finally stops at two brass doors, the burnished finish looking out of place in this damp and moldy place. Stud jerks his chin towards the door and then spins on his heel, disappearing back down the hall. I swallow, and with my heart in my throat, I open the door.

...

I blink, blinded by the sudden white light. I stumble forward, guided by my hands waving in front of me. It turns out that using hands as a guide is not a very trustworthy navigational method.

I run smack dab into a hard chest, sending me toward a path of doom that ends in the linoleum floor.

"Whoa, easy there!" A calloused hand grasps my arm, pulling me up. I blink as I'm faced with a pair of golden/brown eyes and wavy chestnut hair. He grins a blinding white smile and sticks his hands in the pockets of his lab coat.

"I'm Azrael. You must be Phaedra. Please, right this way." He holds out his hand and I'm still so stunned by his shimmering white teeth that I take it. Azrael guides me down the hall until we reach an open room. He takes me to the reclining chair and makes sure I'm settled before going over to a tray set up in the corner and fiddling with the instruments. He pulls on a pair of blue gloves before lifting up a syringe and injecting liquid into it. It's weird. The liquid is reddish and thick. I stare at it, trying to figure out where I've seen it before. The realization hits me like a bucket of cold water. That liquid... it looks startlingly similar to my father's blood splattered on the floor around his death chair. I sit upright, ready to flee when I'm pushed back down. My eyes shoot upward and meet with Azrael's, once so warm and friendly, now frighteningly frigid and cold. He smiles, the look just as chilling as a serpent. "This won't hurt a bit, Phaedra. Not a bitttt..."

Chapter 8

"Ughhh..." Hot light seeps in and takes my headache to a whole new level. Blearily, I open my eyes and take in my surroundings. I'm resting in a camp bed, a flannel blanket haphazardly thrown over my body. There are farming tools all around me, stuffed in drawers, littering the ground, spilling out of containers. Sunlight filters in from holes in the roof, making dancing angels on the ground and that's when I realize that I must be in a barn, or at least some type of shed. I heave myself up, pushing the blanket off of me and leaving it in a rumpled pile on the floor.

"Squawk! Squawk!"

"Ahh!" I stumble backward as a chicken with an attitude darts under my feet.

"Oh goodness, I am so sorry." A young man comes running into the barn, scrambling for the runaway chicken.

"Squawk squawk! Squaawk!" With one last desperate dive, the mysterious man finally wraps his hands around the chicken's middle.

"Whoo. You gave me a run for my money there, Bida." With a laugh, the man plops the struggling chicken back into the coop and then finally turns to face me. His eyes sparkle in the sunlight, turning gold. Tousled chestnut hair waves in the wind and he is easily one of the most attractive people that I have ever met. Which is why I automatically don't trust him.

"I'm so happy you're awake. You gave us quite a scare when we found you sprawled out in the field. I'm Azrael, by the way. It's jolly good to finally meet you." With a pearly smile, he holds out his hand. I stare at his hand for a whole twenty seconds before bringing my eyes up to his. He starts to fidget, getting more and more uncomfortable, until he finally brings his hand to his hair, messing it up even more. I startle at the motion, my body braced to flee.

"Umm, well, Ma's in the house right now, getting supper ready, so if you'll just follow me I'd be happy to escort you." He grins and turns around, hands in his pockets, whistling a little tune. I stare at his back, moving farther and farther away. Who is this *Azrael* and why is he being so nice to me? Does he know who I am? He must, mustn't he? I start to back away, my feet moving from rough wood to damp grass, my footsteps leaving imprints in the damp grass. *Squelch squelch squelch.* I turn around, hesitating for one more second, looking back at the strange man who has offered me nothing but kind words. And then I break into a sprint.

Chapter 9

For a blissful moment, all I hear is the swish of my skirts and my heavy breathing. And then I hear Azrael.

"Wait! Wait, come back! We're not going to hurt you!" I ignored him, my mind set on escaping this place and making my way back to the manor.

"Phaedra, please wait!" His voice rings in my ears. I stop, nearly falling over in the wet grass. I turned to face him, my face leached of color.

He comes to a stop, bending over and resting his hands upon his knees.

"Yes, I know your name. You're the daughter of the richest man alive, for God's sake! So. Please. Just. Stop." He looks directly into my eyes and walks toward me, his footsteps light, as if he's approaching a wild animal that's keen to run off at any moment. I eye him, looking him up and down. He chuckles, his face relaxing.

"I can make it easier if you want." He lifts his arms up and spins around. I snort, a smile playing at the corners of my lips.

"Aha!" Azrael laughs, triumphant. "I made you smile, which means you don't entirely hate me, which means you might let me take you back to the house." He grins, his logic clearly flawless in his mind. I raise an eyebrow in response, surveying him up and down once more before brushing past him, ignoring his outstretched hand.

"I wouldn't say I don't hate you. I mean, I barely even know you. You don't expect me to make such assumptions on the first day of our relationship, do you?"

Chapter 10

I cough, my eyes watering as I step across the threshold of Azrael's house. The smell of essential oils and scents clogs all my senses as I make my way around the stacks of books and recipes that lay scattered across every surface. The only clean surface is the dinner table, which is piled high with every type of food you could imagine: Breads, pasta, vegetables, meat. The scent makes my mouth fill with saliva and I realize then how long it's been since I've last eaten.

"Greetings, greetings! Come, sit, sit." A round, plump woman waddles over, a sleeping baby boy, and a cherry pie precariously balanced in her arms. She places the pie on the table and takes my arm, pulling me over to a seat and pushing me into it. She busies herself with adjusting the plates and glasses.

"Azrael, tell your sisters and brothers to get down here, would you dearie? They were supposed to help me set all of this up but what can you do?" She sighs affectionately and it's obvious how much she cares for her children. I feel a sharp pang in my chest, imagining my father sitting down for dinner and actually talking to me. However, my attention is drawn away from my thoughts as what sounds like a stampede rumbles down the staircase. My mouth drops open as what appears to be an endless stream of children comes running down the staircase. They all stop when they see me, their eyes a collective force of inspection. The one in front creeps forward until she's about a fist's distance from my face. Which is to say, *very* close. I lean back, not wanting to appear rude, but feeling very uncomfortable with this little girl's scrutiny.

"Lilia!" the mother scolds, snapping her towel against the girl's backside. With an *eep!* Lilia scrambles away from me, rubbing her behind.

"Mamaa," she whines.

"Don't 'Mama' me, young lady. You should know better than to crowd guests. Have I taught you nothing?" She huffs and turns toward me, smoothing her face into pity. "I'm sorry darling. Even though she's the oldest she still has lapses in judgment."

I laugh nervously. "It's quite alright. I'm just not accustomed to children."

She laughs and pats me on the back before shuffling over to the stove. "Well, we certainly do have many here! Oh my, I've forgotten to introduce myself, haven't I? I'm Helen, you've already met Azrael, and these younglings are Lilia, Ava, George, Emi, Harry, and this little one in my arms is Oscar." Helen beams and gestures to her children, practically glowing with pride. I wave and have to smile when they enthusiastically wave back. Helen claps.

"Alright now, time to eat. We have plenty!"

Chapter 11

I climb out of the small bed, careful to not wake any of the girls. Silently, I pack a blanket, sweater, and some pieces of bread that Lilia had snuck up earlier, being careful not to leave anything lying around that could indicate I was here. Looking where I step, I pad down the stairs in my stockings remembering where the steps creak from my trek upstairs earlier. Peering around the banister, I slide across the wooden floor, stopping myself at the door. With one look back at the cozy cottage, I open the door and slip out. Or rather I try to. Instead, I collide with the solid chest of Azrael. I stumble back, my socks slipping on the floor and my things going flying.

"Whoa, easy there!" Just as I'm about to fall in a very mortifying way, I'm grabbed by a calloused hand and pulled back up.

"Here, let me help you." Azrael starts to pick up my things, gathering them in his arms. I search for something to say to stop him but come up empty. His brow furrows in confusion as he begins to connect the dots. Looking back at me he takes in my traveling clothes and cloak before directing his gaze back at my belongings. I twist my hands together, waiting for his reaction.

"Phaedra... are you... are you going somewhere?" He looks at me, eyebrows raised in anticipation of my answer.

I open my mouth but nothing comes out. Helplessly, I look back at my door and then back at him. I open my mouth again and finally words come out. "Umm, yeah, actually, I'm going home." I attempt to smile but it comes out more like a grimace. Azrael's eyebrows shoot up even higher and he produces a strangled sound.

"Home? You're... you're going home? Do you know how far away your home is from here? When I found you I was so confused about how you arrived here because the only reason you would be *here* is because you had something extremely urgent that needed to be tended to!"

I gape at him, stunned by his reaction. "Azrael... where exactly are we?"

He laughs, running his hands through his hair. "Phaedra, welcome to absolutely nowhere."

I step back until my back is pressed against the door. I look at him and set my chin. "Nevertheless, I do need to get home as soon as possible. Is there a train or something I can take?"

Azrael turns his gaze to me and something in my expression must make him concerned. "Phaedra... is everything okay?"

I waver for a moment before shaking my head. Memories of that dreadful experience come washing in. My father's body bent over, the blood drained from his body. Anna's head on the floor, blood oozing out. Everything that's happened clouds my brain and overwhelms my senses and yet... I feel like there's more. More to the story. But as I rack my brain all I can come up with is... blankness. Nevertheless, tears spill down my cheeks and drip onto the floor.

Azrael takes a hesitant step toward me, then another, and another. Before I know it, he's wrapping his arms around me. I freeze but he just rests his chin on the top of my head, tightening his hold. Before I know it he's wrapping his arms around me. I freeze, my body becoming tense, but he doesn't let go. Eventually, I allow myself to relax, releasing all of the stress and horror of the past few days.

Chapter 12

"Well, that is quite the story," Azrael sighs, leaning back in his chair. I wait, looking down into my lap like I just discovered the most interesting thing in the universe.

"Hey. Phaedra."

I lift my gaze to his, bracing myself for judgment, scorn, anger that I have brought this to his family, to his home. But all I see is sympathy and kindness. I relax and laugh quietly. "Yeah, I guess it is."

Azrael reaches his hand across the table and covers mine with his own. We stay like that for a moment, reveling in the moment of shared knowledge. Abruptly, he leans back and surveys me for a moment before leaning forward and resting his hands in his lap. I lift my gaze to his, bracing myself for judgment, scorn, anger that I have brought this to his family, to his home. "So, what are we going to do about this?"

I'm taken aback. "We?"

"Well, yeah. You don't think I'm going to let you handle this alone, do you? What kind of gentleman do you think I am?"

I snort, a smirk breaking across my face. I lean forward playfully, putting my chin in my hand. "You, a gentleman? If that's what you think you are then I fear you have been giving me the wrong impression this whole time."

He winces as if I've hit him and places a hand on his chest. "I am hurt! Oh, I don't know if I can handle the pain! Oh, oh, the agony!" He collapses into his chair and flings his hand up to his head. I giggle, the sound traveling through the air and making everything seem all right for the first time in ages.

...

The next couple of days are spent planning how I'm going to get home. Apparently, we really are in the middle of nowhere. There's a train that passes through a town east of here but it won't come for another three months and by then who knows what would've happened back home. I've already missed so much time. Azrael has an old buggy in the barn but we can't take the horses so that idea's down the drain as well. Needless to say, our plan doesn't have much structure. I collapse in the plush armchair and bury my head in my arms. It all seems so hopeless. I probably won't even get to go home at all. I hear the pattering of footsteps. Multiple footsteps. I crack open one eye and find myself face to face with Lilia, Emi, and Harry. I smile and pretend not to have noticed them, putting my face back down. I hear them fidgeting and whispering until finally Harry takes a tentative step forward and pats me on the cheek. I jerk up my head and bare my teeth, growling. Harry scrambles back, colliding with his sisters and knocking all of them down. I laugh and unravel myself from the chair. They look up at me with wide eyes as I stare down at them with hands on my hips.

"Now hasn't your mother ever told you that it's rude to spy on people?"

They all ponder this for a moment and then Emi bolts upright, a smile breaking out across her face. "Why, yes she has!"

I almost snort, my laughter nearly exploding out of me, but I manage to contain myself.

Lilia smacks Emi on the head, scowling at her. "Don't look so proud of yourself! We're not being good *because we're spying on her.*"

Emi ponders this for a moment and then realization dawns on her. "Ohhhhh."

Lilia frowns and shakes her head. "Dumb dumb."

Emi whirls around and stares at her. "What did you just call me?"

Lilia leans forward until they're almost nose to nose. "Dumb. Dumb."

Emi launches at Lilia, wrestling her to the ground. Harry joins in and pretty soon they're tussling and squirming all over the place. They wiggle their way over to me, managing to pull me down with them. That's where Azrael finds us, slapping at each other and tangled up in a mess on the floor.

"Umm, Phaedra?" I pop up, pushing someone's foot away from my face. I brush loose hair away from my face and straighten.

"Yes, Azrael?" He makes his way over, gracefully hopping over limbs. I raise an eyebrow at him, surprised at the ease in which he manages this situation. He blushes a deep red and shrugs. "This happens a lot more than you'd think."

I glance around me, at the bodies that appear to be a mass of arms and legs. I look back at Azrael and he lifts his hands up as if to say, what can you do? I smile and wedge the rest of my way out, nearly falling back in but grasping Azrael's hands to pull me all the way out. I brush the hair and grime off my clothes and turn to face him. He grins and takes my hand, pulling me out of the room. I stumble to catch up, having to walk double my normal pace to match his long-legged stride.

"Where are we going?"

"You'll see." I grin, enjoying the mystery.

I spin around in awe. The stars dot the sky, forming constellations that reach for miles and miles. I whirl around to face Azrael, my eyes gleaming with excitement and my face flush. He grins back, clearly enjoying every moment of my reaction. I laugh, spreading my fingers wide and reaching for the sky.

"What is this place?" I plop down on the grass and pat the spot next to me.

He folds his legs and sits down next to me. He tips his head back and gazes at the tiny specks of light. "I used to come here after my dad died. It helped clear my head and there were so many kids at home… I just needed time… and space. And here is a pretty good place to find both those things." He sighs, seeming more relaxed than I've ever seen him.

I turn to face him, bringing my knees up to my chin. "So, why did you really bring me here?"

He startles and stares at me, trying to remember. "Oh, right! I found a man who's willing to lend us a couple of horses for the buggy so now we can finally take you home. I was thinking we'd go to the village first and then maybe someone there would be willing to take you the rest of the way. I would take you, of course, but my family needs me here and I can't be gone for that long." He looks at me, hopeful.

I shriek in delight, ambushing him with a hug. He wraps his arms around me hard in response and I thank the stars that I've been so lucky as to find this man. Azrael tenses and I let go quickly, worried that our hug has made him uncomfortable. However, he's not even looking at me, and I follow his gaze to the house. He stands up quickly and starts striding towards it.

I follow him, having to run to catch up. "Hey. Is everything okay?"

Azrael halts and looks back at me, smoothing his face into a smile. "Yeah, yeah, of course, there's just something I need to check on, that's all." Without another word, he turns on his heel and keeps on going. I stare at his back in confusion before returning to my spot and waiting, twisting my hands together over and over and over. I lay down, figuring I might as well rest until he gets back. Darkness becomes my friend once again as my eyes flutter shut.

Chapter 13

BOOM. I bolt upright, searching around me for the source of the explosion. My gaze lands on the house and my eyes widen in horror. Flames are licking at the windows and destroying the wooden boards. The fire reaches toward the sky as if they want to escape to the heavens. I stumble to my feet, praying to God everyone's alright but in my heart of hearts I know it's over. Helen, Lilia, Ava, George, Emi, Harry, and little Oscar. *Azrael*. They're all dead. Soul dying, I sink to the ground, splaying my hands on the crumbly dirt, trying to ground myself. I pick up weeds, grass, mud, anything I can get my hands on and smear it on my face, on my lips, in my mouth. It tastes of rot and I think how fitting it is that I'm still alive while everyone who has ever shown me love or care is dead. Always dying, always dead. I laugh, hysterical, my voice rising as I sing. "*Little little boy falls right down. Little little boy digs his grave real well. Little little boy falls right in. Little little boy dies right then.*" I continue singing, the octaves rising until it's a scream piercing the moonlight sky. I hunch forward, pressing my face into the rocks and pebbles, letting them dig into my face, not caring if I bleed. Heavy footsteps creep up behind me. *Crunch. Crunch. Crunch.* A *click* resonates behind me and I feel the cold barrel of death against my head.

"Your time is over, *Miss Phaedra.*"

Laughter fills my throat and my voice cracks as if it hasn't been used in awhile.

"Don't you understand? It always has been." I arch my head up so the barrel presses more firmly into my scalp. I feel no fear, only a cold, harsh, emptiness in my chest.

"Go ahead. Do it."

"Whatever my lady wants." With poison lacing his words, he pulls the trigger. *BANG.* The shot echoes through the sky, spooking birds and creatures out of hiding, forcing them to flee. They run, try to hide. Try to escape. Movement settles. All is quiet. The only activity is a shadow melting into the darkness, leaving the body of a young woman behind. Leaving death behind.

Little little boy falls right down. Little little boy digs his grave real well. Little little boy falls right in. Little little boy dies right then.

CREATIVE
WRITING
WORKSHOPS

THE REVENGE OF FOREVER
by Kayla Macnowski
St. Francis High School, 9th Grade

It's funny how one moment can change your life. One moment we were safe, happy, together. The next moment, my younger sister, Taura, and I were standing over my parents' dead bodies. The lights in the dusty parking garage flickered as tears streamed down Taura's cheeks. Slowly my Aunt Venetta crept out of the shadows. An unsettling feeling washed over me as I sucked in a breath. "How did you get here so fast?" I asked.

Her lips slowly curved into a smile. "You've done a naughty thing, children," she whispered.

***

I slid the knife down the stick and brushed the shavings into the fire. I'm not the same innocent, vulnerable girl I was a month ago when Lennon and I helplessly hovered over our parents' bodies. The murder my brother and I were framed for committing. Lennon walked over to me with handfuls of berries.

"Thanks," I mumbled as he poured some into my hand.

Breakfast.

But then, just as we were laying out our final plans for escaping to our grandpa's cabin, I lost the only real family member I had left. A black truck jerked up next to us.

"Auntie," I whispered under my breath.

"Run!" Lennon yelled, and we dashed through the woods.

"No matter what," Lennon huffed, "keep running."

My eyes stung as my feet pounded on the dusty ground. I had to keep running. My legs burned. I felt the cool wind on my face. Finally, I couldn't run a step further, so I decided to climb a tree. I reached for a branch, jammed my foot in a hole, and pulled myself up. I rested on a branch, laying my back against the tree and dangling my legs down. I tried to keep my breathing quiet while I waited for Lennon, but he never came.

***

Water filled my lungs as I thrashed and gasped for breath. Aunt Venetta grasped me by my collar and yanked me out of the water.

"I'm going to give you one more chance," she rasped. "Tell me where Taura is going!"

I was filled with utter disgust as I lied. "I already told you, I don't know!" I was plunged back into the rusty tub in the dusty dim basement. Water filled my nostrils. Aunt Venetta tugged me out of the water.

"Grandpa's Cabin," I wheezed.

Venetta unclenched her jaw. "There we go," she beamed, grabbing her keys.

I sold my sister out. While I worry this makes me an evil person, I was thinking of a plan. I only needed a little more information, and it would end with my aunt in jail.

"Aunt Venetta!" I called before she left.

"Why did you kill my parents?"

"Silly boy," she laughed, "I didn't kill your parents, you killed your parents."

I looked her stone cold in the face. She didn't blink.

"I told you something, now you tell me something: Why. Did. You. Kill. My. Parents."

"They knew a secret," she whispered, "a secret I couldn't have people knowing."

The secret. The fire. The secret my parents were keeping about the fire was *her* secret.

You psychopath, I thought bubbling with anger. *They kept your secret when they shouldn't have and if I ever get out of here you can be assured, I won't keep your secret!*

My aunt could read my facial expression like a book.

"And apparently you know it too," she said, pressing her lips together.

The echoes of her steps got quieter as she walked away. Aunt Venetta was going to kill me like she killed my parents. While she was gone, I had to escape.

There wasn't much time. I pulled on the knot and tugged it loose. Once my wrists were free, I untied myself from the wall. I ran and jumped to reach the ledge of the dim window. I hit the wall. I tried again, and my fingers barely grasped the ledge. I felt myself slipping. I heard my aunt's footsteps. She was coming downstairs to kill me. I had to hurry. After I pulled myself onto the ledge, I punched through the glass and squeezed out the window. I was free. I had to find Taura before Auntie did.

***

I looked into the shimmery blue water off the end of the dock. I sat swinging my feet back and forth, creating a small current—causing the minnows to flee. I looked across the horizon at the pine trees that smelled like mint. I took a deep breath, filling my nose with a salty sea smell. I had made it. Lennon hadn't. All of a sudden, I felt a cold boney hand placed on my shoulder.

"I thought I'd find you here."

That voice. *Her* voice. Aunt Venetta. My heart raced as my breaths grew sharper. How did she know where to find me? Only one person knew where I was going, and only one person could have told her.

"Freeze!" Lennon yelled. He stood with his feet planted at the end of the dock with a gun pointed at my aunt. Although he looked convincing, I knew he would never fire it.

The color drained from my aunt's face, and she didn't move a muscle.

"Taura, hold the gun," Lennon directed, "and I'll call the police, I have proof that...." his voice trailed off. I knew.

He had a plan to give Aunt Venetta justice. I gripped the gun tightly. I felt like it belonged in my hands. I locked eyes with my aunt. My all too frightening and sickly familiar aunt who seemed to follow me everywhere. My aunt who ruined my life, made sure everything around me crumbled until I had nothing left. My aunt, the lady who murdered my parents that dark and gruesome night in the parking lot. My aunt who made sure I was wanted for the murder of my own parents. Not only that, my aunt who captured my brother. Aunt Venetta. Lennon wanted justice. I didn't want justice. I wanted revenge. I pulled the trigger, watching the bullet spiral through the air. Aunt Venetta fell backward into the lake. Lennon, my innocent older brother, who never knew what I was capable of, let out a scream. Warm red blood pooled around Aunt Venetta, blending with the cool water. She was dead, but there was still a problem: now I was just as evil as she was.

HELLO GEORGE

Children's Storybook by Kristen May
Traverse City Central High School, 10th Grade

Page 2-3

Have you met George?

[illustrations of George's shadow creeping around]

No?

Page 4-5

[Newspaper clippings with titles that say "Strange Creature Living in Unreachable Cave" and "Local Monster That Has Never Been Sighted"]

Page 6-7

Well, he is kind of shy. He likes to lurk in the shadows of his cave, and only comes out when nobody's looking.

[George's cave and little glimpses of him]

Page 8-9

However, perhaps you could convince him to come out of his cave. What do you think?

[Shadow of George's head cocked in question]

Page 10-11

Can you say, "Hello, George"?

[Glimpses of George's feet as he scurries around]

Page 12-13

Oh! I think he likes you!

[Footprints leave heart imprint or smiley face]

Page 14-15

Can you say, "Please come out, George"?

[Each question reveals more of George - his arms and legs are shown on this page]

Page 16-17

There! Did you see him? He poked his head out for you!

[Just his head for this page]

Page 18-19

Can you say, "Do you want to be my friend, George?"

[George's face shown in question, quizzical yet hopeful]

Page 20-21

He waved! Wow, he's a huge fan of yours.

[George waving his entire body shown (shadow)]

Page 22-23

Now let's see if he'll play with you.

[George reaching for a football, baseball, and a rock]

Page 24-25

Maybe if you kick a soccer ball into his cave, George will kick it back! I've heard that monsters like soccer.

[A soccer ball shoots out of the cave]
Page 26-27
Very nice! Let's try something else. How about a game of catch?
[Baseball and baseball mitt in front of the cave with George's arm reaching out]]
Page 28-29
You're the only one George has ever played with! He must really like you!
[Shadow of George's face with a visible smile]
Page 30-31
You know, if you ask really nicely, George might come out and say hi.
[George peeking out of his cave with hearts and smiles floating around him]
Page 32-33

Can you say "I'd really like to meet you, George"?
[George walking, getting bigger each step he takes (shadow)]

Page 34-35

Look! There he is!

"Hello, I'm George. I would really like to be your friend!"   `

[George's full body shown]

The End

NORTH ED WRITERS
STUDIO AT
CAREER TECH

HEULWEN

by Sara Bagley
Traverse City West Senior High School, 12th Grade

A child of the sun, that knew no rain;
her feet light as feathers as she danced across the forest floor.

Shining auburn locks
and eyes of green that reminds one of the waving grassy fields
that sparkle with morning dew.

As a baby, she cried
and the earth shook with every tremble
of her fragile body.

The dirt swallowed her tears,
and the once-blue sky was ousted by
a crowd of dense grey clouds.

Flowers drooped wearily while
bright leaves fell from high branches;
nature wept for her sorrow.

But when she smiled, oh, how she shone.
The world stopped on its axis to catch a glimpse
of her warmth.

Sunflowers perked their heads
as she passed, tipping their faces toward her,
eager to drink in her light.

The wind rushed to be her companion,
floating gently through her hair and whispering
secrets of the woods into her ears.

Birds sang while squirrels scrambled
to be at her feet, chipmunks chattering happily
in small dens nearby.

Her spirit belonged to the forest,
but her heart longed to race through grassy fields –
to run free beneath clear, blue skies.

One dreamy summer day,
she crept to the edge of the woods and tiptoed
into the flowing waves of wheatgrass.

She marveled at the sky,
unobstructed by the canopy of leaves
that had darkened her youth.

Without her, the forest slowly died.
Green vines shriveled up as flowers wilted;
small animals migrated to find new homes.

Bark peeled from sturdy tree trunks,
and beetles began to gnaw at the bones
of each elderly oak.

The forest wasted away,
long forgotten as Heulwen found joy again in
hills and valleys of lands unknown.

COLORS

by Alister Easterwood
Forest Area High School, 11th Grade

yellow and blue shine together
pink and brown are together forever
all colors go together, you see
except when others aren't too keen
I'm orange, I don't want to be with green!
orange said out loud
though it saddened him to think so
but purple wants yellow
and gray wants brown
their hearts in a flurry
but their heads hung down
denying the feelings
ignoring their wants
scared of receiving
the beatings and taunts
but one day they'll blossom
forget the fears
overcome the pain
and face their tears
stand out and be bold
know they're more than enough
be okay with their hearts
be okay with their love

THE LIVES THAT WE LIVE

by Aubrey Flores
Traverse City Central High School, 11th Grade

Oh, the lives that we live
and the way they can vanish in a second

We miss them dearly
and life can seem dreary

But the world keeps burning
the lovers keep dying

How do we continue through the grim of this world
so hideous and horrible this world can be

We find beauty in the little things
but the shadows want to swallow them whole

However, neither are forever out of sight
for good can not live without bad

In the end we'll all vanish
and we'll look back at these funny lives we lived

ODE TO SEASHELLS

by Lily Galnares

Traverse City West Senior High School, 12th Grade

As I stroll along the beach,
I saw them all.
They pile up on the sandy shore
as that salty roaring sea
sends waves that crash.
At first sight
trinkets that make the beach shine.

So many different colors,
so many shapes and sizes.
Some are brown,
or coral pink.
Some are striped like a zebra
or painted with dozens of spots.
They may be smooth like a polished stone,
possibly bumpy like a toad.
Some even have horns
that poke into delicate skin.

In the large crowd of shells
there are individuals that are new,
shiny, and bursting with color,
not a scratch or dent
on their skin.
Others are old
with holes withered
throughout the surface,

algae growing
like a head of green hair.
Barnacles have staked their claim,
glued on forever.

As I walk along the shore
under the setting sun,
a large conch shell resting in the sand
catches my eye.

Questions flood into my mind.
Where did it come from?
How did it come to be?
Did it come from a snail,

Who was washed up from the
deep?
Or was it dragged up here
by that strawberry-colored hermit crab
who once called it home.
Just like its friends
the conch tells a story that I will never hear.

How will its life carry on, I wonder.
It may sit there on the beach
day and night.
It'll listen to the seagulls screech
as they swoop above.
It'll hear the shrieking laughter of children,
and their footsteps
pounding into the sand
as they run by.
Maybe it could hear

the joyful barking
of a happy dog,
its collar jingling
as it trots along the shore.
Eventually
it will break down
becoming nothing more
then little fragments.

I decide to choose the fate
of that mighty conch.
I pick it up and put it in the bag on my back.
It'll be a souvenir,
to remind me of better times.
So in the future,
when I'm trapped on a dark, frigid earth,
I can feel the sun soak into my skin,
and hear the crashing of the ocean waves
once again.

A SILENT FAIRY

by Lily Kolbusz
Kingsley Area High School, 12th Grade

Have you ever heard a fairy?

No?
I figured that would be your response.

Well, wouldn't it be fun to sit down and think about it?
They may sound like bells, the ones on a cat collar, to be specific.
But then that begs the question,
is it one bell being rung or multiple bells hooked
onto a rope being rung at once.
Maybe a fairy sounds like a twinkle.
But then, what does a twinkle sound like?
Maybe a fairy sounds like a symphony.
But then, what instruments would be a part of this symphony?

Hmm, I'm stumped, are you?
I figured you would be but you also might not be.

I'll leave you to ponder on the idea.
But first, let's introduce a new one: maybe fairies don't sound like
    anything.
Maybe they're the absence of noise.
Fairies remind me of a golden red and orange sunrise.
The one on a still lake, where the birds don't chirp, and the bugs
    don't buzz.
A beautiful sunrise in a calming silence.

Hmm, I think fairies are silent, but I'm not sure. What are your
    ideas?

DEAD THINGS

by Eli Pszczolkowski
Traverse City Central High School, 11th Grade

Moss and mold and worms and snails
and wetness and empty and damp.
That shrill smoke scent
of a crawling steel jungle,
preaching the gospel of a twisted construct
instead sings to the breeze a soft melody,
a requiem of sweetness, of decay, of fresh air and of fresh death,
heard by no one.
The figures of creatures, the lions of this jungle,
stand motionless in the tower-lined clearing
like mildewed statues.
The inviting song flutters past ears
that have become nests for cicadas.
A grinning sunbeam, the smog lifted from its gaze,
washes over a blank mannequin face,
its eyes hollowed and filled with weeds.
Its clean white ribs make a beautiful planter
for the colorful fungus that spreads its fingers to every limb
as if it were nerves.
Take a deep breath,
let the spores fill your throat,
let the peaceful poison feed your corpse to the green.
Bury yourself in the teal moss blanket,
and let a brood of worms make your body their home.
Let your skin be overcome by hungry blue mold, layer by layer
inch by inch.
Be calm, have no fear.
Join the silhouettes
of all the dead things here.

A DAY IN THE LIFE
by Emily Rasmussen
Traverse City Christian, 11th Grade

On my bad days, my heart pounds against my chest, but I feel the
  pumping in my whole body.
I hear frantic footsteps, an incessant drum beating faster and
  faster.
On my bad days, I can't get enough air in; I'm suffocating.
A child smothered by a pillow, a diver trapped under a rock at the
  bottom of the ocean.
On my bad days, the world is too bright, too real.
Walls squeezing me to death, neon lights swimming across my
  blurry vision.
On my bad days, I can't think; I can't move.
A raging storm, leaves torn to shreds in a whirlwind, a cinder
  block crushing my bones.

On my good days, I feel a peaceful numbness.
A board game, a crackling fire, nestling together on the couch, a
  warm cat held to my bosom.
On my good days, the world falls into perfect, beautiful rhythm.
A slow acapella song, wispy clouds drifting across a dark canvas
  speckled with stars.
On my good days, I force a smile, and I wonder when
The illusion will fade; the facade will drop, and then, I suppose,
I'll be back to the beginning of this poem again.

BEAST
by Penelope Schuster
Kingsley Area High School, 12th Grade

She's a panther indeed.
Her fur like velvet, her body
black and lean. She's quick
when she runs. She's fierce
and she's mean. Her teeth like
razors, and sharp as
they come at me.

One bite and everything is
red. Oh, can't she hear me
scream? I put my arms up to
hold her back, but she's
kicking me with her feet.
One knock and I feel black soft
velvet surrounding me.

She's a panther indeed and I surrender to my beast.

I AM/YOU ARE

by Makaila Scott

Grand Traverse Academy, 11th Grade

you are the short blonde hair
that i long to run my fingers through.
you are the perfect smile
filled with blue braces.
you are the dark red jeep cherokee
i see everyday in the school parking lot.
you are the beautiful blue eyes i admire
while i'm supposed to be doing algebra.
you are the desk that sits across from me in math.
you are the floral doc martens i want so badly,
limited edition and
too perfect and expensive.
you are the hand i want in mine.
you are the silver chain i see
peeking through the top
of your blue uniform shirt.
you are the tears forming in my eyes,
born from the thought
that i'm not yours.

i am a barely used nikon camera,
resting in a brown leather bag.
i am layered necklaces and
silver metal rings.
i am black winged eyeliner
and short brown curly hair.
i am old records hanging on the wall,

collecting dust.
i am vintage clothes,
a gem found at a thrift store.
i am the many young adult books on my shelf,
waiting to be reread.
i am the random notes,
hurriedly scribbled into a journal.
i am the tens of hundreds of ideas
that i'll never put on paper.
i am the blue ink on my left hand,
shaped into little stars.

ODE TO A CREEK

by Charlie Slawnik

Traverse City West Senior High School, 12th Grade

A small creek
down the hill
behind a house
Overcast
by the lush
green maples and
the flakey, sticky spruces.
Framed and encased,
by the waxy, sweet leaves
of the myrtle,
moving ever closer but never reaching.
The creek,
gurgling quietly,
as it travels
on its way.
Skimming over
the muddy bottom,
everchanging,
never the same.
The creek
ever feeding its neighbors.
The trees
stretching their long
tangled toes,
into the muck on the bank,
searching for food.
The leaves,

dead and dying,
drift aimlessly,
unable to breathe,
or bask,
or drink,
unable to change anymore,
seeking
their final resting place.
The ducks,
to them this is,
their bathtub,
their dinner table,
their way home,
floating weightless,
on their watery RV.
The fish,
playing and dancing,
zipping around
through the wakes and currents,
leaving them behind
to ebb and flow
changing nothing.
The creek
carries on,
casting bright reflections
from its clear green water,
while hiding
anything and everything
in its depths.
This watery marvel
carrying the power to carve valleys,

and shape mountains,
if given enough time.
yet it chooses not to.
Instead
it moves on
as it has and will continue to do.

THANK YOU, SILENCE.

by Ella Smith
Traverse City West Senior High School, 12th Grade

I never realized how much I'd miss something until it was gone.
Surrounded day in and day out by the headaches and heartaches
of the world.
The never-ending screams and sounds of daily life surround my
every move.
Yet I have peace.
At the end of the day, coming in and out of consciousness,
I sit.
Tiptoeing around the room, the lights are off.
I sit.
In that moment I am at peace with myself, my surroundings, my
world.
Everything is quiet.
As my breathing slows, it feels as though the world's breathing is
slowing down as well.
It feels as though everyone around you is experiencing this same
euphoria
even if it's just for a second.
I sit,
legs crossed, like when I was a child sitting on the carpet in
elementary school.
I sit,
straightening my back for the first time in a month.
I sit,
eyes closed, not asleep but so close.

CORRELATION BETWEEN MYSELF, MICE, AND RAIN

by Alexa Sprenger

Traverse City West Senior High School, Alumna

Mice hide when there is rain.
Rain tends to start as a few drops,
falling to the ground,
cascading on leaves, until they reach the dirt.
Nobody notices the rain until it hits them.

Mice hide when there is rain.
Their body is small,
their lungs are even smaller,
a drop of rain feels like a boulder to them,
the rain is crushing,
leaving nothing in its path of destruction.

Mice hide when there is rain.
They look for shelter — a rock, a leaf, a log,
anything will do to escape the rain from above...
the drops are coming faster now.

Mice hide when there is rain.
The water slips through the cracks in their new home,
surrounding them, flooding the safe space they found.
It's too much.

I hide when there is rain.
The mice and I are one and the same.

The rain is like people,
flooding into a building,
unprotected, unsafe, careless.

The rain is like people,
talking over each other,
like thunder overlapping in the forest.
Their voices grow louder and louder with each word,
but no matter how hard I listen —
I can't understand what they are saying.

I need a rock. I need a leaf. I need a log.
I need to hide. I need to run.

I hide when there is rain,
I hide when there are people,
I hide when everything is too much.

I am like a mouse,
scurrying in the woods, trying to survive,
trying to feel safe in a world stacked against me.
People and rain are a constant threat.

But the rain doesn't last.

Once the rain is gone,
the mice and I emerge from the shattered home we found.
There is always another storm on the horizon,
looming, casting a shadow of worry from the uncertainty,
we don't know how long it will last.
How long will we survive for?

The mice and I prepare for another storm.

Mice hide when there is rain,
I do the same,
but at the end of the day — nobody is to blame.

All we need sometimes is just to run and hide.
Let the storm pass, we will survive.
Focus on breathing air into the little lungs, focus on the dark sky
above,
Look for the sun in the distance.
The sun will rise again,
we will be okay.

The mice and I hide from the rain.
The mice and I are both brave.

The mice and I are the same.

ODE TO SHOES
by Henry Trombley
Kalkaska High School, 11th Grade

Oh, my companions
friends of my weary feet
company of sturdy canvas
and soft sole,
you carry me along,
guiding me,
and easing the impact of every
jog
run
and roll.

Marching ever onwards,
easing my way
and providing me protection;
a swordsman's blade,
a warrior's shield.
shoes, too, have lives,
hearts, and souls.

My shoes love the forest
my shoes love to sprint
they adore the momentum of a jog
and they hoard the brush of grasses
upon their worn tread.
They are old, and caring,
they remember my warmth
and they stash it for safekeeping.
And when I take them off

they curl up and rest
at the foot of my bed,
as a cat would,
on its carpet nest
when the day is done.

Symbiotic, in this way
my raggedy converse shoes,
they cradle my feet
and venture with me.
They provide
stability
through creek
and through rain,
through fret,
and through pain.

Oh, my shoes,
without your presence I should
waver and ponder,
sitting steady and stagnant,
idle and longing
for your familiarity,
your warmth, and your luster.

What I would be without you,
oh, my shoes.

FAMILIAR NEIGHBORHOODS (EXCERPT)

by Sam Fikes

Traverse City West Senior High School, 12th Grade

In the distance, there was the low rumble of a plane. Everybody had gathered inside to watch. We took in people from the street for safety. It was not a passenger plane. There was something distinct in the high piercing roar of its engine as it ripped through the atmosphere that was far too violent for any regular flight. As the dot grew bigger it became clear it was directed towards us.

Video cameras hovered above window sills while many crouched motionless. Bright white flashes and arcs of grey smoke sped towards the ground right next to our home. We were only shocked out of disbelief by the deafening thud that shook the tableware in our kitchen with a clatter. A baby started to instinctively shriek and wail. Everyone went running for the basement.

The air was tainted with gunpowder and the faint metallic odor of adrenaline dilating the nasal passageways, quickening the pulse. We were all so scared.

By nightfall we heard gunfire light up the distant city, the occasional boom echoing off the damp basement walls.

Searching our phones, we saw videos on social media of tanks running over innocent people trying to drive away. What does this do to the children? The young men are talking seriously about going to war. They have their whole lives ahead of them.

It's day two, and there are warplanes being shot down over familiar neighborhoods. The young men left to fight as volunteers. They may be killed in days. Everyone is making plans to leave. It almost feels too late. The room is constantly spinning, and the slight look of shocked nausea rests perpetually on the faces of everybody here. Air raid sirens whine in the distance for hours.

Whole cities have gone underground to hide away from rockets and bombs. What will happen to them, to all of us? So many people everywhere so powerless to stop this.

THE WALL NOT MEANT TO BE BROKEN
(EXCERPT)
by Taryn Spencer
Kalkaska High School, 12th Grade

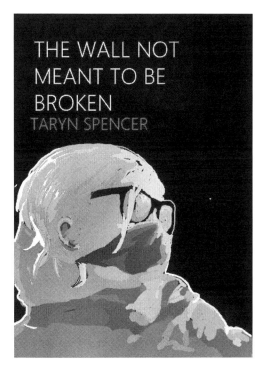

Moonlight poured into Xena's room, shrouding him in a pale blue glow. He stared at the moon while his mind sat and soaked in a sweet, bitter plot of revenge. Even though it was deemed impossible, the target was in his world for the first time... and he had some matters to settle with them. While he stared at the moon, though, he kept finding small loops and inconsistencies in his plan. He turned his head to a small cactus on his nightstand and began to speak in a whisper. "I've gotten wind of the next target being in our hometown. I know, I know, I thought it was impossible too but my buddy even gave me a residential address and everything. I think... the time has finally come. Yes... if this address is legit, everything is going to change for us."

The cactus gave Xena nothing but silence, which caused Xena to face-palm. "Of course! I'm such an idiot, I never *told* you. Someone I've had a grudge against for a long time is in town, Al. I've waited for this since the day I was born and brought into this miserable world. There are some... issues with the circumstances I'm under, but I'll never get another chance like this, so I'm gonna have to get it right the first time." Al the cactus still only stared, holding back the encouragement Xena was so desperately pining for from him.

Xena kept talking as if he didn't care, or just simply never noticed. "You know what they're saying, Al? They're saying... *The Writer* is here, in our world, in this town. I don't know what I'm going up against but I'm ready for anything! The Writer will pay for what he's done!" He broke off into an evil cackle, gathered his hair into a small bun as he always wore in battle. "I wasn't going to leave until tomorrow night, but I'm... I'm so excited I can barely sleep, ha. I'm just... so excited! I- Al won't you talk to me? Can't you see that this is important to me? Honestly, you're being so selfish! The *Writer!* For Goodness sakes, and you have *nothing* to say to me? Look, I'm sorry I accidentally over-watered you last week but this is a little bit more important than your silly grudge. It was an accident, okay? I'm *sorry.*"

Al still said nothing, and just sat with inanimate eyes while Xena stumbled around the room making a fool of himself as he gathered his supplies. For an assassin, Xena was oddly careless of his weapons and the state of his room. Al often witnessed this routine of Xena driving himself mad over how he can't find a hair tie or how he's ended up in urgent care because he won't put a lid on his coffee cups. The idiot has a bounty over his head, you'd think he'd at least get a lid...

"Fine, whatever." Xena muttered, pulling on a long, leather coat that fell to nearly his ankles. He began to shove various items into its many pockets. "I wasn't looking for your validation anyway, but hey- before I take care of The Writer, I'll ask him for something for you okay? Then we can be good again, yes?"

Silence. Xena nodded reassuringly to himself, and silently snuck out his bedroom window, perching his feet on the first ridges in the wall his feet could find. "I'll get something prosperous and beautiful out of the Writer for you, Al! I promise! And then, I'll take him down!" Xena climbed down the wall, parting ways with his one and only true friend and ally. He gripped the dents in the bricks tightly, knowing full well that this could be the last time he ever saw Al. *It's a good thing I over-watered him before. He's angry with me now, but if I don't come back... he's going to be glad he had that extra water. I don't think anyone else in the world would even notice my departure in case of the worst. Maybe the nice elderly lady that likes to buy plants from my shop, but there's no telling if she would care enough to stop by my place and take over that precious life for me.*

Despite Xena's clumsy and unkept nature, when his shoes landed on the wet concrete there was no sound at all. He brushed off his shirt and grinned at his silence, which was one of the few things he prided himself on. *Not an assassin, but a ninja!*

The address was in a part of town he had never visited before, and he felt sort of put off by that. He'd been on this job for as long as he could remember and ended up in what he thought was every hidden passway, crack and corner his town had. When he looked at the address his buddy had slipped into his pocket, it was like a completely new section of the town dropped onto the earth from the wizard man in the sky.

He shoved his hands into his pocket, as a former sprinkle in the sky began to buckle down into cold pellets. It wouldn't have been the first time he had been mistaken about his surroundings.

On a mission around two years previous, he had walked into the completely wrong bar, and searched around for a passenger who would never arrive.

No discouragement bubbled in him, though. Only exhilaration, and a mild hunger. Xena set off silently into the night, off to fight his longest and most irritating villain yet: The Writer of this very story.

THEODORE AND FRANKLIN: A MURDER MOST FOWL

A Play by Annabelle Ackley
St. Mary School - Lake Leelanau, 11th Grade

<u>Cast of Characters</u>

THEODORE   A pig who works as a detective. Has a serious but friendly demeanor. Wears a sweater vest with a tie and a top hat.

FRANKLIN   An over-excitable duck who is being mentored by Theodore. Wears a sweatshirt and a deerstalker hat that he thinks looks cool. Wants to be a detective.

MARTHA   An old cow who discovered the body. Is very emotional and sweet. Scares easily. Wears a modest sweater, a long skirt, and glasses

CLAIRE   A creative girl who loves playing with her toys. Wears a cute and frilly pink dress.

<u>Scene</u>

A farm somewhere unspecified in the US. There is a red barn off to the left with a few buckets lined up near it. A toy chicken lies on the ground next to the barn. On the right side of the stage is a table with three chairs.

Present day. In the early afternoon

SCENE 1

AT RISE: MARTHA sits on a chair at the table to the right. She is nervously fiddling with her skirt. THEODORE and FRANKLIN enter. FRANKLIN carries a small memo pad and a pen to take notes on what everyone says.

THEODORE

Hello, Martha. My name is Detective Theodore and this is my protégé, Franklin.

(FRANKLIN waves.)

We are investigating the unfortunate demise of a chicken named Grace. I understand that you are the animal who discovered Grace's body?

MARTHA

Yes, that is correct. What a tragedy indeed.

(MARTHA sniffles and wipes at her eyes. FRANKLIN rolls his eyes, pulls a handkerchief out of his pocket, and hands it to MARTHA. MARTHA loudly blows her nose.)

THEODORE

Martha, could you describe the scene of the crime to me? Please go into as much detail as you can.

MARTHA

Well, I was headed to the barn for breakfast time. The cows and chickens eat at the same time since our meals are so different from each other. I thought I was the first who arrived there this morning, but it turned out that I...

(MARTHA blows her nose again. FRANKLIN takes note of what MARTHA is saying)

That I wasn't! And then I saw little Grace's body right there and... and it was just so terrible!

(MARTHA wails loudly and falls to her knees, wraps her arms around FRANKLIN's legs, and cries at a comical volume. FRANKLIN tries to scoot away, but MARTHA holds on tight and is dragged along on the ground. FRANKLIN pats MARTHA's shoulder awkwardly.)

FRANKLIN

I don't really get why you're so upset. It's just Greedy Grace who died, that's all. If anything, we should be--

(THEODORE quiets FRANKLIN with a glare.)

THEODORE

I'm terribly sorry for making you recall those memories. Discovering Grace must have been an experience that you wish to forget.

(MARTHA lets go of FRANKLIN's legs. Composes herself.)

MARTHA

No, it's all right. I'm more concerned about getting behind who did that poor girl in! I mean, I don't have any idea why someone would want to be rid of Grace! She was such a lovely girl, you see.

FRANKLIN

No, she really wasn't very lovely at--
>   (THEODORE swats FRANKLIN on the back of
>   the head and glares again. FRANKLIN sticks his
>   tongue out at THEODORE when he's not looking.)

THEODORE

Yes, yes. Very lovely indeed. Martha, did you notice anything strange about Grace's body when you came across it? Was there anything that was, say, out of the ordinary?

MARTHA

I'm sorry, Detective, but I just can't seem to recall anything stranger than the fact that poor Grace was dead.

THEODORE

Yes, that must have been quite shocking. (Standing up) Well, thank you for your time, Martha. Please do let us know if you remember anything significant.

MARTHA

I will, detective. Thank you.
>   (MARTHA exits left. Once she is gone, THEO-
>   DORE turns to FRANKLIN.)

THEODORE

Franklin, I must urge you to be more careful with your words. If you are too insensitive, it may be hard to get the information you need from a witness or suspect. Do you understand?

FRANKLIN

Yes, sir. I'm sorry.

THEODORE

Good, good. Now, let's go and examine the barn. Franklin?

FRANKLIN

Yes, coming, sir!

END SCENE

SCENE 2

AT RISE: THEODORE and FRANKLIN are looking around the barn. Grace's dead body, a toy chicken, lies on the ground next to the barn.

THEODORE

Ah, yes. The scene of the crime. What do *you* make of it, Franklin?

FRANKLIN

You—you're asking *me*, sir?

THEODORE

(Dryly) Yes, of course I am. You *are* training under my wing. Of course, it is a metaphorical one because I am a pig and pigs do not have feathery appendages attached to their torsos, but you get my point, yes?

FRANKLIN

Yes, sir! R-right! Um, well, we should probably check the body first.
> (THEODORE nods. FRANKLIN picks up the toy chicken, examines it all over.)

Let's see... I can't find any blood. No cuts or scrapes, no lacerations, no stab wounds either. Gah!
> (Fed up, FRANKLIN tosses the chicken over his shoulder.)

Why is investigating so hard!

THEODORE

(Annoyed) Don't become flustered, Franklin. Have you checked under her feathers for any bruising?

FRANKLIN

(Sighs) No, I haven't, sir.
> (FRANKLIN goes back to pick up the chicken again, examines it more thoroughly now.)

THEODORE

Franklin, could you assist me in examining the surroundings?
> (FRANKLIN stands up suddenly and dashes over to THEODORE, stopping right next to him in a stiff salute.)

FRANKLIN

Y-yes sir!

(THEODORE nods at him to look around.)

Um, well, it's the feeding barn. The troughs are all lined up there.
I guess the other chickens left the troughs alone so that we could
investigate, since all of them are full... woah!

(FRANKLIN drags the word out as his voice rises
in realization.)

The troughs! They're not completely full! Usually there's more
seed in these, but they're all missing some. But what does it mean?
Maybe the other chickens just took a little bit to hold themselves
over for dinnertime?

(FRANKLIN looks around the feeding area again.)

Wait a minute, one of these is empty!

THEODORE

Oh? Do you know whose trough this is?

FRANKLIN

I think it might be the one that Grace eats out of!

THEODORE

I see. This information may become essential to this case. Good
work, Franklin.

(FRANKLIN beams and jumps in the air, pumping
his fists.)

FRANKLIN

Thank you, sir.

THEODORE

It would probably be best to go somewhere to think on this information that we've gathered, yes?

FRANKLIN

I'd like to do a little more looking around the farm, sir. I've already found something important, so I think I might find another clue if I keep going. Can I meet you later?

THEODORE

Yes, that's fine. I'll see you in an hour or so.
> (He exits, leaving FRANKLIN alone with the toy chicken.)

FRANKLIN

(Kneeling down) Hmmm...
> (FRANKLIN looks intently at the chicken.)

That's interesting. There's some food here on the ground where she was lying. I wonder...

END SCENE

SCENE 3:

AT RISE: THEODORE and FRANKLIN stand in front of the table. THEODORE paces back and forth in deep thought.

THEODORE

Hmm, yes.

(Nods)

I believe we have collected all of the evidence that we need.

FRANKLIN

There are no external wounds, no signs of a struggle, and no weapon of any sort to be found. How are you so sure that there's no more evidence for us to find?

THEODORE

Oh, my poor, sweet, ignorant Franklin.

(THEODORE pats FRANKLIN's shoulder in sympathy. FRANKLIN frowns and shrugs the hand off.)

Can't you see? The devil, as they say, is in the tiny little details! The barn, Franklin! Think about the barn.

(THEODORE taps his finger on his temple.)

What was odd about the barn?

FRANKLIN

I know what was odd about the barn, sir. It was the seed that the chickens eat. Well, there was a quite unusual amount of it.

(FRANKLIN also begins pacing.)

It seems like the feeding troughs usually have more seed inside of them. I should know, I *am* one of the animals who eats it. What I mean to say is that I think it is strange that there was less seed inside of the feeding troughs.

THEODORE

And you would be precisely correct, Franklin. Well, anyway, yes. You are correct about the amount of seed. There was too little of it to plausibly be a filling meal for a chicken.

> (THEODORE takes a deep breath and clears his throat in preparation for his big speech.)

As you know, the troughs were not filled enough when we looked at them. It struck you as odd, and it struck me as well. I thought: "Why would the feeding troughs be lacking the correct amount of seed for mealtime? The farmers know the correct amount that we all need to stay healthy, so what was different this time?" And then I began thinking about Martha and—

FRANKLIN

Martha *definitely* didn't do it, sir. She's the only one at this barn who actually liked that greedy chicken.

THEODORE

No worries, Franklin, I wasn't suspecting Martha. She's the only one here who wouldn't lay a finger on anyone no matter the circumstances.

FRANKLIN

Oh, well, that's good. I was a little worried for a moment there. You know, I've been thinking a lot lately.

THEODORE

Thinking? (Smugly) Well, that sounds like an improvement from how you usually do things. What have you been thinking about, Franklin?

> (FRANKLIN sighs.)

FRANKLIN

I'm thinking that, well, maybe that it *wasn't* someone else who killed Grace.

THEODORE

(Surprised) Really, now? And just what brought you to that conclusion?

FRANKLIN

Since there were no external injuries, sir, I started thinking about the internal stuff. The body was a little too fresh for proper bruises to form, so that's why I wanted extra time to wait around. It didn't really pay off, though, since no bruises actually appeared.

THEODORE

Well, I suppose you did try, but I've already figured out the cause of Grace's death to be–

FRANKLIN

I'm not done! I didn't find any bruises, but I did find some food scattered around on the ground near Grace's body. And, when I opened her mouth, there was more seed inside.

THEODORE

(Staring intently at FRANKLIN) Just what are you trying to say?

FRANKLIN

I think that, well, what if Grace choked while eating her breakfast? It all makes sense! The other troughs were missing some seed, so maybe she snuck some from each one before the other chickens got there and then rushed to finish her own food? Grace was pretty greedy, but she wasn't stupid.

THEODORE

Yes, I see. I'm very impressed with you, Franklin. That was a job
well done, I'd say.

    (THEODORE graces FRANKLIN with a rare
    smile. FRANKLIN grins wildly.)

FRANKLIN

So what do we do now, sir? Will we tell the other animals what
really happened?

THEODORE

That is precisely what we will do, Franklin.

    (THEODORE and FRANKLIN step away from
    the chair and move to center stage. THEODORE
    opens his mouth to announce the verdict, then
    pauses and shakes his head. Nods at FRANKLIN,
    who looks up with wide eyes. THEODORE smiles
    and nods.)

FRANKLIN

You–you want *me* to announce it? But this is your case.

THEODORE

You're right, it is my case. However, I am not the one who solved it,
am I? If you so please, Franklin, it is your right to give the verdict
of this case, not me.

FRANKLIN

Okay. Thank you, sir!

    (Takes a deep breath)

Animals of the farm, great and small: through careful investigation, we have cracked this case! I have discovered the perpetrator of the crime and their motive.

> (A pause.)

So, without further ado, the true crime and the animal who committed it is...

> (FRANKLIN raises his arms and opens his mouth to announce it, but he and THEODORE collapse to the floor. The stage goes dark and they disappear. CLAIRE walks onstage carrying two toys that resemble a pig and a duck.)

CLAIRE

So, without further ado, the true crime and the animal who committed it is—

> (CLAIRE waves her arms around dramatically before stopping abruptly. It seems like she hears something from offstage.)

Yes, Mama, I'll be right there!

> (She runs offstage to the left, leaving the pig toy sitting in the middle of the stage.)

END PLAY

NEWLYWEDS

A Play by Sara Bagley
Traverse City West Senior High School, 12th Grade

<u>Cast of Characters</u>

BONNIE   Elderly, but a few years younger than JIM. Married to JIM for 63 years. Wears reading glasses and an old wedding ring. Regretful, and wishes she could have a "re-do."

JIM   In his 80s or 90s. Married to BONNIE for 63 years. In mid-late stages of Alzheimer's and is largely unresponsive.

JESSICA   Late twenties. Style is dressy casual. She's high strung, specific about her ways of organization. Married to ALEX, newlyweds, and newly living together.

ALEX   Same age as Jessica, touchy about kitchen organization and his peanut butter. Casual wear. Married to JESSICA, newlyweds.

<u>Scene</u>

Upstage/mid-stage, there are two "apartment" layouts. On stage left, there is a rug with two armchairs, a small table next to one, and a coffee table. This is Bonnie & Jim's apartment. On stage right, there is another rug of a different style, with an end table and a loveseat arranged around it. This "apartment" belongs to Jessica & Alex. There are also a few boxes lying around on stage right, maybe labeled with different rooms. There are invisible "doors" downstage in front of these areas, and the room left downstage is the hallway. A light is focused on the "doorway" in front of Alex & Jessica's place.

Present.

Scene 1

AT RISE: A mug, a box of tissues and a bottle of pills sit off on the coffee table on stage left. A purse sits on the end table on stage right. Dishes clink in background.

BONNIE is reading a Guideposts magazine in one armchair on stage left.

JIM is leaned back in the armchair next to the small table on stage left, asleep. There's a blanket draped over him.

ALEX is relaxing on the loveseat on stage right, on his phone or laptop.

JESSICA is offstage right.

BONNIE

Oh, my word. Look here, Jim! It's our old neighbor... what was her name? Callie? Candice? (Beat.) Candy!

(BONNIE looks up, excitedly showing the magazine to her husband.)

187

Our old neighbor Candy, the young blond thing with that beautiful garden? She's in this magazine I'm reading, it's got her name here next to this wonderful story about legacies. It says she's written a book!

> (BONNIE watches Jim, eager for a reaction. She eventually looks down, slightly discouraged.)

You always said she'd do something special.

> (BONNIE begins to read again. A few beats pass, she turns a page. JIM shifts, waking up a little. He blinks around. BONNIE looks up, a blend of hopeful and attentive. She looks around him.)

Oh, dear, you don't have your tea. (She sets the magazine aside.) Ahh, I'll get it. Don't want you to go and break anything on your way to the kitchen.

> (BONNIE laughs lightheartedly and sets down her book before retrieving the mug from the coffee table. She sets it down on the small table next to where JIM rests.)

There you go, dear. I'll get your meds as well.

> (JIM looks at her, his head moving slightly as she moves. BONNIE shakes out a few pills from the bottle and hands them to him. It takes JIM a while to speak.)

JIM

(Slow, fragmented.) Thank you.

BONNIE

Always, darling.

> (JIM uses his strength to lift a shaky hand and pop the pills in his mouth. BONNIE helps him lift the mug. JIM takes a small sip and sets it back down with BONNIE's help. BONNIE smiles sadly at him for a moment and sits back down, opening the magazine once again, and beginning to read.)

JESSICA

(Offstage, loudly.) Alex. (Beat.) Alex!

> (BONNIE perks her head up, perhaps startled. She listens to their conversation, setting her book down open on her lap. Jim shifts in his sleep.)

ALEX

(Yelling back, distracted) Yes babe?

JESSICA

Finish those dishes, please?

> (Enters from stage right and comes up to where ALEX is seated. She grabs a purse off the end table.)

I've got to run and get the photos I printed.

ALEX

(Getting up.) Photos?

JESSICA

From the honeymoon? I'm going to make that scrapbook!
Remember?

ALEX

Yes. I remember now. (Starts to head off stage right where JES-
SICA entered from.) I've got these, don't worry about it. Do you
mind grabbing me a 7Up while you're out? And some crunchy
peanut butter please? I'll love you forever.

> (ALEX exits. More dishes clink, a cupboard is
> opened. BONNIE resumes reading.)

(Offstage, shouts.) The knives don't go here!

> (JIM shifts again, obviously disturbed. BONNIE
> notices him do so and watches him carefully, still
> listening.)

JESSICA

Yes, I can grab those for you. And what do you mean? (She exits
stage right, where she came. Speaks from offstage.) Yes, they do. I
rearranged the kitchen over the weekend while you were at work.
(She re-enters.)

ALEX

(Re-enters right behind JESSICA, frustrated.) Why? Everything
was fine!

JESSICA

(Nonchalant.) I dunno. I felt like it.

> (BONNIE shakes her head, almost laughing.)

BONNIE

There they go again, Jim.

ALEX

(Frustrated still.) Jess... I only care about one thing. And it's keeping the kitchen organized the way I like it. Please?

JESSICA

It's not that big of a deal! Give it two days, and you'll have everything down again. We only moved in two weeks ago! It isn't as if it's
been that way for years.

ALEX

(Slightly annoyed.) Fine, but if anything else is in a new spot, I'm
not putting away dishes until you put it all back.

JESSICA

(Complacent.) Yeah, yeah, all right. I think that was the only thing
I seriously moved around, except maybe the bowls.

ALEX

(Exits off stage right quickly.) Jess, for the love of- (Beat, another
cupboard bangs open.) Good news. They're still where I had them.

JESSICA

Thank the Lord.

        (JESSICA and BONNIE both chuckle. BONNIE
        shakes her head and begins reading again.)

ALEX

(Offstage.) I heard that. It's not funny!

JESSICA

I just didn't think it'd be an issue! I promise to warn you next time. I'm not used to living with someone else yet.

ALEX

(Calmer.) All right... (He pops his head out from behind the curtain stage right.) Oh, hun, we need some toilet paper too!

JESSICA

What?? I just got some two weeks ago! (She hurries back off stage right.)

ALEX

(Offstage.) I dunno what to tell ya, babe. We used it?
            (BONNIE reacts to their bickering, silently laugh-
            ing a little. JESSICA re-enters, ALEX on her tail.)

JESSICA

(In disbelief.) How did we use that much already?! I bought a two-pack. I figured it would get us through this week, at least until I got groceries!
            (ALEX scratches the back of his neck, and JES-
            SICA rubs her temple. BONNIE shakes her head.)

BONNIE

(Slightly amused.) My, my. This reminds me of the little tiff they had last week. Over the thermostat, remember that darling? I'm glad I held on to our old manual, or else they might still be struggling with it!

JESSICA

(Frustrated.) Now I've got to go to Walmart, too.

ALEX

(Throws his hands up.) Don't blame me!

JESSICA

(To ALEX.) You used it too! A two-pack used to last me a good three or four weeks!

ALEX

Well, yeah, but there's two of us! We kind of need to buy double the toilet paper now.

JIM

(Slowly waking up. He groans quietly.) Huh?

BONNIE

(Snaps to attention. To JIM.) What was that dear?

JIM

(Grumbles a little.)

BONNIE

(Gazes at him. A moment passes.) It's just those newlyweds next door, love. Go back to sleep, it's okay.

> (As JESSICA and ALEX talk, BONNIE exits off stage left. JIM turns and goes back to sleep. BONNIE re-enters with a pack of toilet paper. She walks downstage, through her "door", past her husband and carefully leaves it in front of the apartment "door" on stage right. JESSICA and ALEX

(cannot see her, nor vice versa. BONNIE goes back through her "door", returns to upstage left where she has been seated.)

JESSICA

(Compromising.) Okay. I'll just get some while I'm out.

ALEX

(Comforting.) We'll get the hang of this. I'll see you later?

JESSICA

Yeah. I love you.

ALEX

I love ya too, Jess. (He sits back down on the couch, resuming his reading, game, etc.)

(JESSICA hurries downstage, out the "door." She almost stumbles over the toilet paper left there.)

JESSICA

Huh? (She looks around.) Hello? Whose is this? (Beat.) Hello?

ALEX

(Loudly.) What is it, babe?

JESSICA

Toilet paper. (She keeps looking around for the owner.)

ALEX

(Distracted.) Well, I suppose our prayers have been answered!

JESSICA

Yeah, I guess so. (She picks it up and walks toward Alex, then off stage right. She re-enters without the toilet paper.) I've still got to get the photos, so I'll be back.

ALEX

Okay. Love ya.

JESSICA

Love you too. (She turns away and heads downstage out the "door", confused. She walks off stage left, crossing in front of BONNIE and JIM's apartment.)

BONNIE

Nothing a little mysterious magic can't fix.
> (BONNIE chuckles, pleased. She pauses and looks at JIM for a long moment.)

I fixed it for them, Jim. (Beat.) You'd be proud. (Beat.) I can almost hear you now. That's my Bonnie, you'd say.
> (JIM shifts in his sleep.)

BONNIE

(Sadly.) And that's my Jim.

> (BONNIE drops her gaze, slowly picks up a new book and begins reading. Brief blackout. Stage lights come back on, and JESSICA re-enters from stage left, passing in front of BONNIE and JIM's apartment and then walking upstage through her "door" on stage right.)

She's holding an envelope, creamy peanut butter, and a bottle of 7Up.)

JESSICA

(Excited.) Alex! The pictures turned out beautiful. I'm so excited.

ALEX

You'll have to show me! Let me take that stuff from you.
          (ALEX takes the jar from JESSICA's arms as she
          sets down the other things on the end table.)

Jess, babe, this is creamy peanut butter.

JESSICA

(Anxious.) It is?? Oh no, I must've grabbed the wrong one. I was in a hurry to get everything before the photo counter closed.
          (Over the following, BONNIE shakes her head and
          sets her book to the side. She exits stage left and
          brings back a jar of crunchy peanut butter. Like
          earlier, she goes downstage out her "door", crosses
          to stage right, quietly sets the peanut butter down
          in front of her neighbor's "door", then crosses back
          to stage left and into her "door" to sit in her chair.)

I'll go grab the right one! We can just look at the pictures later.

ALEX

(Frustrated.) It's fine, I can deal for a few days. (Beat.) Let's just see if we have any left, okay?

(ALEX and JESSICA exit off stage right. Beat. BONNIE should be setting down the peanut butter as ALEX re-enters and says the following line.)

ALEX

(Enters right.) I'll just go grab some right now.

BONNIE	JESSICA
(As she re-enters her apartment.) They ought to be all right now. (Beat.) What's that? (She looks at JIM as if he's talking back.) I know, I know, darling. I thought they could use it. (She goes back to reading.)	(Enters stage right behind ALEX.) Are you sure? I can come too, or I can get it. Or I'll just come with you, that's easy.

ALEX

(Annoyed.) Sure, Jess. (Beat.) Let's get going. I really wanna be home before the dinner rush hits downtown.

(ALEX walks downstage out their "door" with JES-SICA in tow and kicks over the jar of peanut butter. He looks down.)

ALEX

What the hell?

JESSICA

What?

ALEX

Peanut butter. (He picks it up.)

JESSICA

Was it just sitting there?

ALEX

Yeah. I kicked it over by accident. (Beat.) What is this doing here?? Did someone set it down and forget it, or something?

JESSICA

(Confused, weirded out.) I don't know. The same thing happened with that toilet paper earlier! And that manual we found last week.

BONNIE

(Looks content, listening.)

ALEX

(Confused.) For the thermostat? I thought you dropped that out here. (Beat.) Maybe I should knock on doors or something. (Studies the jar.) It is crunchy, though.

JESSICA

Nope... (Beat.) Well, regardless, that's perfect!

ALEX

It kinda is. (He relaxes, more content now.) Um, back inside, then? (Beat.) I'm sorry for being a jerk.

JESSICA

It's all right, love. Next time, I'll just bring you with, okay?
> (JESSICA and ALEX walk back upstage through their "door", then ALEX exits off stage right with the peanut butter as well as the soda bottle.

JESSICA sits on the loveseat. BONNIE smiles at the resolution. JESSICA's phone rings.)

Hello? Oh, hi Mom! (Beat.) No, we're not busy. I just got back from the store. (Beat.) Dad wants to come over? Sure! I miss you guys. I have the photos from me and Alex's honeymoon, too! It's perfect. (Beat.) See you in a few!

ALEX

(Offstage, loud.) Who was that?

JESSICA

(Loud.) My parents! They're coming over!

ALEX

(Stressed. He re-enters from stage right.) When?

JESSICA

(Excited.) Twenty minutes-ish, I think. I'm excited! They said they'll bring some pizza from that one place that they like on the east side of town!

ALEX

(Panicked.) Jess- the place is a mess.

JESSICA

(She looks around.) Oh God, you're right. (Also panicked. She points to the different boxes lying around as she speaks.) We need to put out those towels they gave us for the wedding! Oh God, we need to hide the decorations your friends gave us. Where won't they look?

ALEX

I don't know! They're your parents. (Beat.) Why didn't you say no??
Or try to stall them a little more?

JESSICA

I couldn't just say no! You just said it, they're my parents.

BONNIE

Well, Jim, I do think it's time I finally pay them a visit. I'll be back
in a jiffy.

> (ALEX and JESSICA hurry to move boxes offstage
> right and straighten up the place. JIM stays still
> and silent. At the same time, BONNIE sighs, stand-
> ing up and walking downstage out her "door". She
> crosses to stage right to the front of ALEX and
> JESSICA's apartment, facing upstage and standing
> at their "door." A doorbell can be heard.)

ALEX

(Offstage.) That's not them, right?

JESSICA

(Offstage) It's hardly been a minute!

ALEX

(Offstage.) Go see who it is!

> (JESSICA enters from off stage right and goes
> downstage to see BONNIE standing there at the
> "door". A spotlight lights up where they are stand-
> ing. ALEX re-enters from stage right and joins her
> after a moment.)

JESSICA

Hello? Who are you?

BONNIE

Hello, dears. I'm your neighbor. (She gestures to stage left.) And one thing I do have to say about this place, is that we have some frightfully thin walls. (Beat.) Now, I've done my very best to help lately.

ALEX

(Interrupting, confused.) Help?

BONNIE

Yes, help. (Gentle tone, suggesting.) The toilet paper, and the peanut butter?

JESSICA

(Confused, processing.) That was you?

BONNIE

(Smiling.) Yes, that was me. The thermostat manual, too! (Laughs.) Anyways, I've done my very best to help today, but I do hope that this silly bickering won't continue, eh? Toilet paper runs out and having to eat the type of peanut butter-

JESSICA

(Interrupts.) Okay. Um, thanks. We'll be going now.

> (JESSICA looks at ALEX and grabs his hand. JESSICA tries to pull ALEX back into their apartment. He fights her at first as BONNIE continues speaking.)

BONNIE

(Surprised, tries to continue.) The, um, type of peanut butter that you don't like as much truly isn't the end of the-

>(The light on the area shuts off. JESSICA and ALEX retreat upstage into their apartment at the same time. BONNIE looks surprised and a little put-off.)

BONNIE

(Beat.) I... I suppose I'll be on my way. (BONNIE looks down. She pauses upon hearing voices come from inside the apartment. She listens.)

JESSICA

Can you believe that meddling old lady? (Beat.) Helping, yeah, right. That was downright creepy!

BONNIE

(Sad, quiet.) I would hardly call it meddling; I was helping... (She trails off.)

ALEX

(Genuinely.) Shh! She might hear you. She's been listening through the walls, remember? (Gestures to stage left.)

JESSICA

(Slightly quieter, looking in the direction of BONNIE's apartment.) Well, then she might get the idea that she's not helping.

ALEX

(Reluctantly agreeing.) Yeah... but, like, what if it's a personal thing?

(Looks at him.) Then she can figure it out somewhere else. We're not her little experiment. We should be able to argue in our own apartment without old ladies thinking that they know what we need to do!

> (JESSICA stays silent for a moment. BONNIE's shoulders drop upon hearing this. She trudges slowly back to her apartment "door", heading upstage through it and sinking down into her chair, close to crying.)

We've got a few more minutes before my parents get here, we should finish cleaning up. (She looks around.)

> (JESSICA and ALEX continue working on their apartment, maybe heading onstage and offstage to fetch/hide things. At the same time, BONNIE begins speaking.)

BONNIE

(Weakly.) I suppose they've got a point. I won't be a bother any longer. (Sad, to Jim.) I don't know what I did wrong, love. I wanted to help. They were arguing, and it reminded me of me and you, and all the little fights we used to have. (She laughs tearfully.) About the groceries, and your sister coming over, and where we'd hang the wreath every Christmas. (Beat. She begins to cry.) I wish I could go back; I'd put the wreath next to the window every single year, just how you liked it. And I'd stop buying that old oatmeal you hated. I was so convinced you'd come to like it someday.

> (BONNIE looks at JIM, who has his eyes open but is unmoving. She waits, as if she's listening to him.)

It's not that easy, darling. All the company I have is my magazines! (She stops in horror.) I'm sorry, I can't believe- (Beat.) You're right here, and I said that. Oh, Jim, I'm sorry. (Sobs.) You're here... but you're not. (Silence for a few beats. She stands, crossing over to him using a tissue to dry her cheeks before picking up his hands and holding them in hers.)

> (BONNE gazes at JIM, still teary eyed. He slowly moves hands to be around hers, and weakly attempts to squeeze her fingers. She looks down, her voice shaky.)

I love you too, Jim.

END PLAY

THE STRAIGHT WHO THOUGHT HE COULD

A Play by Alister Easterwood
Forest Area High School, 11th Grade

Characters

JULIA RICHARDS	A sixteen year old girl with long brown hair and brown eyes. She can be seen wearing jeans and a hoodie. Not very outgoing or sociable. Best friend of KAYDEN and TYLER'S love interest.
KAYDEN HARRIS	A seventeen year old boy with short ginger hair and blue eyes. He is tall and lanky. Likes to wear basketball shorts and a hoodie. Very outgoing and is well known by everyone. Best friend of JULIA and friend to TYLER.
TYLER WELCH	A sixteen year old boy withdyed black hair and hazel eyes. He wears t-shirts and jeans with combat boots. He is considered weird by most but he does have a small group of friends. Friend to KAYDEN.

SETTING
History room in Newhigh High school.

TIME
Present. 8:05 in the morning.

SCENE 1

AT RISE: JULIA is sitting in a chair at her desk, writing in her journal. She's sitting in the middle of the room, surrounded by clumps of desks. There is really bright lighting. There are shelves filled with thick and heavy books. The room is empty except for JULIA.

KAYDEN

(Enters stage right)

(Grabs chair from desk across from JULIA.

Pulls up chair so he's sitting closer to JULIA)

Dude! Did you hear?

JULIA

(Makes a confused face)

Hear what?

KAYDEN

You know Tyler?

JULIA

Yes?

KAYDEN

He likes you.

JULIA

(JULIA'S eyes widened)

What? Why?

KAYDEN

What do you mean why? What's not to like?

JULIA

(Groans and covers her face with her hands)

That's not the issue! I just really *really* don't like him. He doesn't give me good vibes!

KAYDEN

Ohhh. I see how that could be a problem.

JULIA

It's fine. As long as he doesn't mention it I won't worry about it.

KAYDEN

(Looks to the side and rubs the back of his neck)

Yeah. About that...he may or may not be planning on talking to you this hour.

JULIA

What?!

KAYDEN

And he might be planning on asking you out.

JULIA

(Grabs KAYDEN'S arm in alarm)

Tell me you're joking. Please tell me you're joking.

KAYDEN

I'm sorry! He was talking to me and the guys about it. I thought it would have been good for you.

JULIA

How would that be good for me?! You know I don't like him like that.

KAYDEN

Well you never go out or do anything. You don't even talk to anyone but me.

JULIA

(Offended)

Yes I do!

KAYDEN

I hate to break it to you but online friends don't count. You don't even read like the cliche girls in those books. I just thought that maybe if you gave him a chance you would open up more.

JULIA

Why would you even think we would be good together? We're nothing alike!

KAYDEN

Exactly! You guys would balance each other out! Like peanut butter and jelly.

JULIA

Kayden, I really don't think that a sandwich is the equivalent to the situation you just put me in. And you know talking to people makes me nervous. You could have just told me that you wanted to set me up with someone.

KAYDEN

If I told you you wouldn't have agreed.

JULIA

I'm still not going to agree.

KAYDEN

C'mon, Jules. Just give the guy a chance. He has a Jet Ski!

JULIA
(Sarcastically)
I'm sorry, how does that have to do with me still not liking him?

KAYDEN
(Puts hand up in defense)
Hey now. No need to be rude.

JULIA

I'm rude? You just made a guy think he had a chance with someone, encouraged him even, even though you knew he had absolutely no shot in hell in getting with them. And no one cares if he
has a jet ski!

KAYDEN

Excuse me? I do! Have you ever seen this man's jet ski? It's beautiful! And how was I supposed to know! You never talk to me about
these kinds of things. You could be into chicks for all I know!

JULIA
(Head whips to KAYDEN in alarm)
W-what? No!

KAYDEN
(Looks at JULIA curiously but ignores her excla-
mation)

Okay...? The point is I don't know anything about your romantic life. I just wanted to help both of you.

JULIA

I get what you were trying to do but come on. I don't even know his last name.

KAYDEN

Okay, I see where you're coming from. But he's a nice guy! Sure, he might be a little creepy...off-putting...ugly...but he's nice.

JULIA

I don't care if he's nice, that's not even the bare minimum. And don't be mean, he's not even ugly. You of all people don't have the right to judge.

KAYDEN

What's that supposed to mean?

JULIA
(Faces KAYDEN and looks him up and down)
Bro...you literally look like a pigeon.

KAYDEN

Really? First of all, pigeons are cool. Secondly, you're built like Fix-It Felix.

JULIA

Screw you! I'm the average height for a female!

KAYDEN

No, you're not.

JULIA

At least I don't look like the tube man outside of car dealerships.

KAYDEN

Don't even go there. You simp for Danny Phantom.

JULIA

Danny Phantom is hot!

KAYDEN

Oh my god, just go out with him! He's a nice guy and-

JULIA

(Interrupts)

I don't want a guy!

KAYDEN

(Pause)

...what?

JULIA

(Waves hands in panic)

No! I uh-I meant like-you know-nice. No nice guys.

KAYDEN

You *don't* want a nice guy?

JULIA

(Nods head rapidly)

                    KAYDEN
              (Laughs)
Dude, are you sure you're not a little--
                    (Flicks wrist in a downward motion)
                    (Continues to laugh)

                    JULIA
              (Sighs and keeps looking at KAYDEN)

                    KAYDEN
              (Notices and slowly stops laughing)
Wait...are you...?

                    JULIA

Look...Kayden...

                    KAYDEN

Are you gay?

                    JULIA

I've known for a while, I was just...I was looking for the right time
to tell you and it never--

                    (TYLER enters stage right)
Julia! I've looked everywhere for you!
                    (Walks up to JULIA and ignores KAYDEN
                    completely)
Julia...there is something I have come to ask you.

KAYDEN

(Standing up and grabbing Tyler by the shoulder)

Tyler! My man! It's been a while. We should catch up, ya know, somewhere else. That isn't here.

(Starts to guide TYLER off stage but he stops him)

TYLER

Can't it wait? I was kind of in the middle of something.

(Gestures to JULIA with a discreet look)

KAYDEN

Uh, yeah I can see that...but um...I wanted to talk to you about something. Really important. Like, now.

(Tries to guide Tyler off stage again)

TYLER

(Stops KAYDEN)

What are you doing? We can talk later.

(Tries to walk back to JULIA)

KAYDEN

I wanted to talk to you about...

(Looks at the desks around him desperately. Sees a book and picks it up. Holds it up)

This book! It's a really good book. I was just reading it and I just know that you will love it! Do you want to read it with me?

(TYLER opens mouth to say something but Kayden keeps talking)

You know what, let's go read it together, pal.

TYLER

(Moves away from KAYDEN and walks over to JULIA)

Julia...you look gorgeous this morning. You're glowing.

JULIA

(Gives KAYDEN a knowing look over TYLER'S Shoulder. Laughs nervously)

Thanks. I moisturize.

TYLER

(Sits down where KAYDEN was sitting and scoots chair forward. He takes hold of JULIA'S hands)

Julia. There is something I've been meaning to tell you for a while now. I wanted to wait for the perfect time to do it. I was going to do it at your birthday party--

JULIA

(Interrupts)

I never invited you to that--

TYLER

(Lets go of one of JULIA'S hands and puts a finger to her lips.)

(Whispers)

Shhhh. Let me do the talking.

KAYDEN

(Looks at wrist that doesn't have watch on it)

Wow, look at the time! Tyler, we should really get going! That book isn't going to read itself.

(Points at door behind him with thumb)

TYLER
(Looks back at KAYDEN, annoyed)
In a minute. I'm *trying* to have a moment here.
(Turns back to JULIA)
Now, as I was saying before I was interrupted--
(KAYDEN rolls his eyes)
I have been wanting to tell you something for a while now. Julia Richards, I've known you since the beginning of the year. You're beautiful...funny...smart...

KAYDEN
She actually got a C- in Algebra 2--

TYLER
(Look back at KAYDEN sharply without letting go
Of JULIA'S hands)
Can it, pigeon boy.

KAYDEN
(Looks up and mutters)
I swear...

TYLER
(Turns back and smiles at JULIA)
I know how people see me. They think I'm a loser. Weird. An outcast.

JULIA
What?

TYLER
(Looks down and sighs, shaking his head sadly)
I know, hard to believe, right? But, Julia-

(Looks back up at JULIA)

I can be better with you.

JULIA

Tyle--

TYLER

(Interrupts)

I know a lot of people think I'm scary--

KAYDEN

(Interrupts. Walks up and stands by JULIA. Looks

Down at JULIA)

It's true. I've seen it. Gives me the heebie-jeebies.

(Pretends to shudder. Addresses TYLER)

So maybe you should walk out that there door

(Snaps fingers and points to door)

And spare Jules the fear. Tender soul this one.

(Ruffles JULIA'S hair)

JULIA

(Fixes hair quickly)

For real. It's my weakness.

(Nods in fake sadness)

TYLER

I know that we don't know each other that well yet, and it will be
intimidating at first. But we can do this together. So, Julia...will you
be my gi--

KAYDEN

NO!

TYLER
(Moves back slightly)
Excuse me?

KAYDEN
I--well...you see--

JULIA
(Interrupts)
Tyler...I really appreciate the um...thought that you put into this.
But I'm not looking for a...guy right now.

TYLER
Julia. Honey. I don't think you fully understand what I'm asking
you.

JULIA
Trust me, I do. I'm just not interested.
(Takes her hands out of TYLER'S)

TYLER
W-what do you mean? I love you.

JULIA
No.

TYLER
Yes.

JULIA
No.

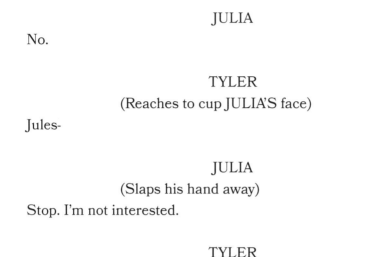

TYLER

Yes!

JULIA

No.

TYLER
(Reaches to cup JULIA'S face)

Jules-

JULIA
(Slaps his hand away)

Stop. I'm not interested.

TYLER

Why not?! I'm the perfect guy! I would take you out on dates, buy you stuff, love you!
(Stands up abruptly)
I don't understand!

JULIA

Tyler, I don't even know you that well. I don't want to be in a relationship with you. Or anyone for that matter.

TYLER

Like I said, we can get to know each other. I don't get why you're being so difficult about this.

KAYDEN

Dude. You really want to be the one talking about being difficult right now. She said no, just let it go.

                              TYLER

This has nothing to do with you, Kayden. Actually, why are you still
here? Wait...

                    (Look of realization)

Oh my god. I get it now.

                    (Takes a step back and looks at KAYDEN and
                    JULIA)

                              JULIA

Get what?

                              TYLER

You guys are together.

                              KAYDEN

What?

                              TYLER

No, it makes perfect sense now. You got mad when you heard me
talking about her and wanted to make me look like an idiot, so you
told me to ask her out knowing she would say no! Wow, you really
are a character, Kayden.

                              KAYDEN

Tyler, we're not--

                              TYLER

                    (Interrupts)

You know what, it's fine. I don't even care. I wouldn't want to be
with someone who had the mind to date you. There would have to
be something majorly wrong with them.

JULIA

Hey!

(Steps closer to TYLER)

Don't talk about either one of us like that.

TYLER

(Slides chair back away from JULIA)

Really?

JULIA

Yes.

TYLER

(looks JULIA up and down with disdain)

You don't...you don't look gay.

JULIA

(Sarcastically)

Oh! Sorry about that.

(Flicks wrist in downward motion)

Is that better?

TYLER

You don't have to be a jerk about it.

KAYDEN

Jerk? You want a jerk, I'll give you a jerk.

(Reaches for TYLER but JULIA stands up and blocks him)

JULIA

Kayden, stop it! He's not worth it.

Whatever.

> (Stands up and walks a few feet away from JULIA
> and KAYDEN. Turns back to them)

When you decide to be straight again you know where to find me.

> (Exits stage right)

KAYDEN

Julia, I am so sorry.

JULIA

> (Rolls her eyes)

Don't apologize for other people's actions. I know you were just trying to help. I really appreciate the thought.

> (Pulls KAYDEN in for a hug)

Thank you for standing up for me.

KAYDEN

> (Wraps his arms around JULIA'S shoulders)
> Anytime, Jules.
> (Continues to hug for a moment)

You know...there's this girl in my Chemistry class-

JULIA

Don't even think about it.

END PLAY

JUSTIFIED MURDER

A Play by Makaila Scott
Grand Traverse Academy, 11th Grade

Cast of Characters

Vincent Williams	Eighteen years old. THEO'S best friend, VICTORIA'S boyfriend. Almost always sounds irritated.
Theo Stevens	Seventeen years old. Has a slightly flamboyant personality.
Harold Stevens	Father of THEO and uncle of VICTORIA.
Victoria Stevens	Seventeen years old. Mostly rude to everyone. Her mental health issues show through the way she moves physically and how she speaks.

Setting

Secluded family mansion in the English countryside. About four hours outside of London. It's a massive mansion filled with vintage/antique furniture. The family calls it 'the country house' and it is surrounded by fields and woods. There are no houses or villages/towns anywhere near it. It looks like a castle and was built in the late 1800s. Props: 1970s telephone, four armchairs or two armchairs and a sofa, side table, coffee table, lamp, tea set, luggage bags, men's clothes, bloody knife.

<u>Time</u>

Mid to late October, the late 1970s.

SCENE 1

AT RISE: The stage is set as a parlour room. A small table is next to an armchair and a sofa with books, a phone, and a lamp on it. A larger table sits between the sofa/chairs with books and a tea set on a tray.

                                VINCENT, VICTORIA, and THEO sit on the armchair and sofa.

VINCENT

Murder?

VICTORIA

Yes. That's what I said right?

VINCENT

Like actual, real murder?

(VICTORIA nods her head)

So, I just want to make sure I understand you correctly, you want to murder Harold? Your uncle. And Theo's father.

VICTORIA

I know it sounds mad, okay, I know. But- he's a *really* bad person Vin.

VINCENT

God, you are actually mental, aren't you?

VICTORIA

(looking to THEO)

Theo, I mean you live with him. You're gay, for God's sake, and he's a homophobic arse.

THEO

I know. That's why I agree with you. Not necessarily the killing part, but I agree that he doesn't at all deserve the life he has.

VINCENT

Did you even hear me Victoria? You. Are. Messed. Up. In the head!

VICTORIA

(still ignoring VINCENT and talking to THEO)

Thank you. I'm not completely mental, okay. I was supposed to keep this a secret, I told her I wouldn't talk about it, but last summer, when my friend Alice was here with us, Harry raped her. She was scared to talk to the police about it, so nothing ever happened, Harry was never punished for it. After it happened, I found some of the other women he hurt. It was difficult because Harry basically paid for their silence. It's not fair. Alice still has a hard time being around men. She hardly goes out of the house alone anymore because of what happened. We need to do something. We need to bring justice to the evil that resides in this house. It's been a whole goddamn year since what happened to Alice, and I just can't stand the fact that nothing's been done about it.

THEO

I know. He did that stuff to the housekeepers. That's why we don't have any staff here anymore. Back when the staff was still here, I just couldn't handle witnessing it anymore, that's why I left and moved to London. Whenever I had a male friend over, my dad would yell at them, saying they should go to hell for being friends with a- I don't even want to say the word. One time, when Michael and I were still together, my dad walked into my room and saw us kissing. He punched me and then started beating Michael and then threw him out of the house, told him if he came back he'd kill him. Michael had to go to the hospital after what my father did to him.

VINCENT

Shit, Theo, I'm so sorry. I didn't know any of this.

THEO

(starts to cry)

You know, I tried to do it before. Kill him. I tried, and I couldn't do it. Why? Why couldn't I do it?

VICTORIA

(getting up and sitting by THEO)

Because he's your dad. No matter what happens, he'll always be your dad and it's just so fu–

THEO
(standing abruptly)

Let's do it. I can't take it anymore. I don't deserve everything he's putting me through. All those people he hurt- they don't deserve it.

VICTORIA
(stands next to THEO and holds his hands)

Are you sure? If you're not okay with like, actually ending his life, we could- I don't even know. I guess there are other ways to put an end to this, but I just think murder is the most effective way to do it.

VINCENT
(standing between THEO and VICTORIA)

Guys! No. You guys, we just- we can't. This is *murder* we're talking about! He's never actually done anything to me, but I've always gotten a bad feeling about him. Murder though? It's absurd! A mental and ridiculous idea! But, I mean even if we did ever do it, could we actually get away with it?

VICTORIA

Vincent, for Christ's sake, I think about getting revenge all the damn time. I want- no, I *need* to do this. For Alice. For Theo. For all of the people Harold hurt.

VINCENT

Alright. You're right. I mean, God knows he won't stop if we don't do something. I just- I'm scared. What if we get caught? What if he ends up hurting us when we try to kill him?

VICTORIA

We'll just have to come up with a good plan. We have to think of every little detail. It'll be difficult of course, but with the three of us, with the pain we all have, I think we could do it. We're in a secluded rich guy's mansion four hours from London.

(THEO begins to walk offstage)

Theo? Where are you going? We've got to make a plan.

THEO

I'm going to kill my father. I need to do it now. If I wait any longer I'll change my mind.

(continues to walk then turns around)

Aren't you guys coming?

(VINCENT and VICTORIA follow him offstage)

SCENE 2

AT RISE: The stage is set as the same parlour room.

THEO and VINCENT walk onstage in silence. They sit gently on the sofa.

VICTORIA

(walking onstage after them holding a bloody knife)

Bloody hell.

THEO

What are you gonna do with that?

(gesturing to the knife)

VICTORIA

(with one hand, pushes the tea set off the tray and
sets the knife on it carefully)

VINCENT

That works I guess.

(with heavy irritation in his voice)

Love, you've got blood on your arms. And your face. And your shirt.
And in your ha–

VICTORIA

I KNOW! Vincent, do you think I don't know there's blood all over
me? I just killed someone for Christ's sake!

(puts her head in her hands and starts crying)

THEO

(walking over to where VICTORIA sits and kneels
in front of her)

Hey, hey, love it's okay. You're alright.

VINCENT

I'm gonna go get you a washcloth to clean yourself up okay? It'll
be okay love.

(touches VICTORIA'S hair lovingly and walks
offstage)

VICTORIA

(to THEO)

Theo. God, what is wrong with me? Am I bloody completely
mental?

THEO

There's nothing wrong with you Victoria. You were brave. You did something that will keep so many other people from getting hurt.

VICTORIA

No, you don't *get* it. I practically begged for my parents to take me to the doctor a few months ago because I was feeling like hell all the time; I- I mean I was sad for no reason, I would lash out at my mum and neither of us would even understand why. And I had these *terrible* thoughts about hurting myself and other people. I was diagnosed with Manic-Depression, depression, anxiety, and personality disorder. And that's not even the worst part! No one was willing to get me the help I actually needed, and my parents, *my own parents Theo!* They wanted to lock me up in a mental hospital.

THEO

Vic, I'm so sorry. I–

VICTORIA

(standing and wiping tears off her face)
I'm fine. What about you Theo? I worry about you, about how you'll be after all this is over. Are you okay? Your father's gone, so like that means you don't have any parents anymore.

THEO

I don't know. I'm so confused right now. I thought I'd be fine, I didn't expect to actually be *sad*. I can't say that I'll miss him- I think I'll just miss the idea of him? I should be more happy right? I mean I can finally live- without him tormenting me and hurting me and telling me what a massive goddamn disappointment I am every day.

>(now crying)

God, this is so pathetic.

VICTORIA

>(pulling THEO into her arms)

It's not pathetic Theo. It's okay to not know how you f–
(telephone rings, interrupting her)

>(pulls away, startled, and both look at the phone with wide eyes)

THEO	VICTORIA
Should I answer it?	Who the hell could it be?

THEO

I'm just gonna answer it. Yeah. It's fine. Yeah...

>(picks up the phone)

Um, h- hello? (pause) Oh.

>(shoves the phone into VICTORIA's hands)

It's your mum!

VICTORIA

>(putting the phone to her ear)

H- hey mummy. (pause) Yeah, we're having a good time so far. (pause) You- you want to talk to Harry? He uh, he's- (pause) Um... oh he's not here. (pause) Um, well we got here and- uh and Harry wasn't here. (pause) I don't know. He just always says to make ourselves at home if he's not here when we come to visit.

>(VINCENT walks back onstage and sits in the chair with a cloth in his hand)

(pause) Mum really, it's fine. We're all nearly adults. (pause) We'll be fine alone, I promise and if anything happens, I will call you.

(pause) Yes. (pause) Alright, we're fine, I've got to go. (pause) Okay. I love you Mum. Bye.

(puts the phone back on the receiver)

Oh my god I think I had an actual heart attack.

THEO

Alright, lovely. So... now that people will be under the impression that he's away, maybe we should, like, pack a suitcase with some of his things and throw it away so it looks like he was actually gone.

VICTORIA

That's actually a brilliant idea Theo. You sure you're not a natural born killer?

(winks and both laugh)

VINCENT

How can you two laugh right now? You're acting like this is all some twisted joke! Are you bloody psychopaths?

THEO

Vincent, what the hell man?

VICTORIA

You're acting like we did this alone. Did you forget that you made the choice to kill him too? I mean it's 1977 for Christ's sake, this stuff happens all the time!

VINCENT

You mean we're like Ted Bundy then, just killing like it's not a big deal? Well in case you didn't know, this is a massive deal, Victoria! And I'm sorry you felt like you needed to get revenge for your friend, but it's not her, or my fault, or anyone's fault that you're manic and completely mental!

VICTORIA

I hate you. If you think I'm so mad then just break up with me because I know you don't really love me anymore!

(now crying)

(VINCENT and THEO are both silent)

I- I gave you my whole heart, Vincent. And you just- tossed it aside like it didn't matter at all. And I loved you so much. I don't even know why! You were always such a prick. But you know what? I'm going to go home after this, and still want you. I'll miss you.

(laughs a breathy laugh and wipes away tears)

Why the hell do I even bother?

(storms offstage)

(it stays silent for a moment)

VINCENT

(running his hands through his hair)

Bloody hell. What has she gotten me into?

THEO

Are you joking? What was that?

VINCENT

You're taking her side? I can't believe you, you're supposed to be my best friend.

THEO

No. No, you can't do that! You can't act like you're the victim of your and Vic's relationship. You can't even begin to imagine the hell that she lives in!

(VINCENT is silent)

Fine. Be that way.

VICTORIA

(comes back onstage after a moment, carrying a
suitcase and an armful of HAROLD'S clothes and
other belongings. she sits by THEO and silently
packs the suitcase)

THEO

Thanks Vic. I think the smartest and easiest way to get rid of
everything, including uh, the body, is to burn it all in that massive
furnace oven thing in the cellar.

(VICTORIA nods and tries to half smile at THEO.
both walk offstage with the suitcase and tray holding the knife)

VINCENT

Fine! Don't speak to me, don't let me help you. You can do it on
your own!

(picks up the stack of books off the table,
throws them, and sits down with his head in his hands. after a
moment he walks over and picks up the books, setting them gently
back on the table. he then walks offstage, visibly upset)

SCENE 3

AT RISE: The stage is set as the parlour
             room.

             VICTORIA is alone, packing a
             suitcase with some of HAROLD's
             clothes and other belongings.

VICTORIA

(sitting on the couch muttering to herself)

Bloody mental. Bloody mad. Bloody insane. Bloody hell, you bloody psychopaths. Murdered someone, you deserve to burn in hell.

VINCENT

(walks onstage silently as VICTORIA still mutters to herself)

VICTORIA

You deserve to be locked up in a bloody madhouse. A bloody mental hospital.

(sees VINCENT and groans)

What do you want?

VINCENT

I- I came to see if you're okay. Actually no that's not true. I came to apologise. I'm really sorry for earlier, Vic. For what I said. You're not mental. You just don't have anyone helping you, and that's not fair. *I* want to be that person that you can trust, that person that can offer you help. I've been such an arse. I am truly sorry, Vic. I'm going to try to be better. I really want to be better to you. I just really hope you'll be able to give me another chance. I know I've already had my second chance, and I blew it. I've probably blown the third and fourth chance too. I really love you a lot Vic, and I honestly don't know how I'd live without you.

VICTORIA

(walks to VINCENT and looks at him without saying anything, then hugs him)

I wasn't lying earlier when I said I'd always want to be with you. Somehow I'll always be able to forgive you.

(pulls away and a little and smiles)

I know I should feel bad about killing my uncle, but I feel like a weight has been lifted off my shoulders, off my heart. I feel good now. I feel like I'll be able to look at Alice without feeling guilty somehow. I always used to feel like it was partially my fault because he's my uncle.

(THEO enters)

Hey, you doing alright?

THEO

(smiles)

Yeah, I'm okay. I'm glad you two made up, I heard the whole thing. Most romantic thing I'll ever hear.

VINCENT

Yeah, I came to realise that no matter how guilty or glad any of us may feel about this, we're in it together. We all took part in this. We can't tell a single soul about this.

THEO

We should make a pact. To *never* tell anyone about this. To always be here for each other.

VICTORIA

You're right. We did this together, we'll be bonded to each other forever because of it.

VINCENT

Should we do a blood pact?

THEO

That would be cool, but it seems a little cult-like.

                    VICTORIA
(smiling a little)
Uh, I think we've all seen enough blood for tonight.
                    (holding out her pinky finger)
Let's do it old school. Pinky swear?
                    (THEO and VINCENT hold their pinky fingers to
                    VICTORIA'S)

                    THEO
                    (pulling VINCENT and VICTORIA into a hug)
Ah, I love you guys.

                    VINCENT
Love you too mate. You know what's kinda funny? The fact that it's
October, and it's cold and eerie makes this whole situation seem
like something you'd read in a book.

                    VICTORIA

Guys?

VINCENT   THEO
(both on edge)
What's wrong?   Everything alright?

                    VICTORIA
(laughs)
I think we're all bloody mad.
(all three look at each other, smile, then laugh)

                    END PLAY

THANK YOU, JUNE.

A Play by Ella Smith

Traverse City West Senior High School, 12th Grade

Cast of Characters

JUNE   Girlfriend of BROOKES, caring, kind, and gentle towards others. Heart is filled with love. Healing from a past relationship.

BROOKES   Boyfriend of JUNE. Weirdly good at gaslighting and is definitely a male manipulator.

KAHLIL   JUNE and BROOKE'S friend. Has known BROOKES since college and met JUNE through the relationship. Very good at listening.

Scene

The shared apartment of JUNE and BROOKES, the living room. There is a couch in the corner of the room with a chair on the left side of it. A side table sits between the two with a glass on it. The apartment is a mess with boxes scattered around. In the kitchen, there is a table with beer bottles and old newspapers thrown on it. It's an open room with a door on the same wall that leads to a hallway and another door on the other side that leads to the bedroom.

The present. Around 6 or 7 at night, it's dark outside with the darkness flooding into the room through the open window.

SCENE 1

AT RISE: BROOKES sits in a chair, drinking whiskey on the rocks. Moaning and groaning to himself after every sip.

JUNE sits on the couch, hugging her knees into her chest. Her head on her knees. Silently crying to herself.

JUNE
(Looks over to where BROOKES is sitting and shakes her head)

We both know this isn't healthy anymore. Stop lying to yourself BROOKES.

BROOKES
(Takes a deep breath and sets drink down)

I didn't wanna fight, I really didn't.

JUNE
Stop, BROOKES.

BROOKES

I didn't wanna fight. (Raises his voice) Why did you start a fight?

JUNE

Why did *I* start a fight? Me, starting the fight? Did you forget why you started yelling at me in the first place?

BROOKES

What are you on about?

JUNE

You really forgot?
        (Beat)
You have got to be kidding me. All of that screaming for you to forget 20 minutes later? My god, you're pathetic.

BROOKES

It's not the time for your bullshit, JUNE, just tell me what I did wrong, I'll apologize and everything will be fine. Just like usual.

JUNE

Not this time, BROOKES. (Takes a deep breath) You really don't remember? How much did you have to drink?

BROOKES

That doesn't concern you, JUNE.
        (Takes another drink)

JUNE

Doesn't concern me? (Raises voice) Doesn't concern me?
You know what? I'm done.

(Stands up and exits stage right)

BROOKES

(Yelling to the other room)

JUNE, stop it, you're overreacting. Did you forget how much fun we had?

JUNE

(Enters stage right)

Do you remember how scared I was to date you? Not because you were scary but because I had been in love before and it wrecked me. Turned me into someone I never want to see again, remember that?

(Beat)

But then I met you. And it was like all of my problems were solved, I had never been happier.

BROOKES

Exactly, so let's move on from whatever this is.

JUNE

And I had always told myself I would never fall in love again. Because I knew all it brought was pain and suffering yet I continued, I kept going, I acted like nothing bad would ever happen. You made me oblivious to things that hurt me, YOU hurt me. I was vulnerable, I was so vulnerable with you.

BROOKES

(Interjecting)

You call this vulnerable? All you're doing is yelling at me.

JUNE

(JUNE ignores BROOKES)

I opened up my chest for you, ripped out my own heart, and gave it to you. Do you know how much that hurt me?

(Beat)

I had built up my defenses my whole life, carried a suit of armor for god's sake. Then you showed up. You're no different from the rest. You're another one of the stupid people, who wander into my stupid life, and stupidly choose me?

(BROOKES waves at JUNE in a dismissive manner)

Why me? I gave you a piece of me, arguably the most important piece, and you... you opened it up, you dug, explored, and played around.

When you realized there wasn't anything left in there for you, you left but parts of you were still inside. You continued to dig around in places you didn't belong. You knew you had no place there, Why did you stay? Why did you continue to make me suffer?

It was like you took me hostage. You got inside of me and slowly tore me apart from the inside out.

BROOKES

(Sternly)

JUNE, stop it.

JUNE

Don't... don't.

(Beat)

You took my trust, that wall I had built up and you destroyed it. I can't believe that four years of a relationship meant nothing to you.

I can't believe you were able to just leave me sitting by the side of the road in the rain. Cars drove by, some stopped. They asked me if I was ok, if I needed a ride home. I told them not right now. Home doesn't seem like the best place to be. Can you believe that? I still considered this hell hole to be my home.

BROOKES

I pay for this place, how could you call it that? You don't pay a single *dime* to live here.

JUNE

I could live with someone else, they wouldn't kick me out. They would answer when I called.
        (Smugly)
Funny enough, one of our friends actually drove by, I didn't even have to call him.
        (Begins laughing and crying while speaking)
He did a double-take when he saw me sitting there, he pulled over and ran to me. I told him I was ok. He didn't believe me. He gave me that blanket.
        (Points to a blanket draped over the couch)
That's why we were arguing, that's why you were angry at me. That's where the blanket came from. Our friend, when you left me by the side of the road. In the rain.
        (Beat)

BROOKES

Which friend?

JUNE

Really? That's what you're concerned about? Not the fact that you screamed in my face about a stupid blanket? Not the fact that you thought I cheated on you because of a stupid blanket? You are unbelievable.

BROOKES
(Judgmentally)
Which friend?

JUNE
You have got to be kidding me. You're not serious, are you? Which friend? Does it really matter which friend helped me not get frostbite because my shitty boyfriend left me by the side of the road? You kicked me out of the apartment. Whatever, I don't care. But then you felt the need to throw me into your car and drop me off somewhere I didn't even know. I had no idea where I was or what I was going to do. I had no money or any of my belongings with me and you drove off. I screamed your name hoping you would stop but no, you never looked back.

BROOKES
(Visibly upset)
JUNE I'm not gonna ask again, which friend?
(Throws glass onto the floor)

JUNE
(Gasps and begins to shake head)
Stop... stop, please. BROOKES, I'm pregnant.

BROOKES
...what?

JUNE
I'm pregnant BROOKES. Seriously, pregnant.

                    BROOKES
JUNE I swear to God if you're bullshitting me right now.

                    JUNE
Why would I lie about this BROOKES? Why would I lie?

                    BROOKES
        (A smile slowly begins to form on his face)

JUNE that's... that's incredible. You are going to have my kid.

                    JUNE
You can't be serious. BROOKES we cannot bring a child into this
world when we fight like this almost every day.

                    BROOKES
        (Smugly)
JUNE that wasn't a question, you're having the baby.
        (Begins to slowly walk towards JUNE)

                    JUNE
        (Her body tenses as BROOKES walks closer to
        her)

        (Someone knocks on the door to the apartment.
        Everyone stops in their tracks)

        (JUNE begins to walk over to the door but
        BROOKES stands up in front of her, blocking her
        way to the door)

JUNE

Move.

BROOKES

Who's at the door, JUNE?

JUNE

I don't know, why would I know?

BROOKES

JUNE, don't lie to me. Who's at the door?

JUNE

(Gritting her teeth)

I... don't... know. That's why I told you I don't know.

BROOKES

Fine, then I guess you won't mind if I answer it?

JUNE

Be my guest.

(She scoffs as she sits down on the couch)

(BROOKES opens the door to see KAHLIL)

BROOKES

Man, this might not be the best time.

KAHLIL
(Looking past BROOKES)

JUNE... oh, thank goodness you're ok.

JUNE
(Looks over to the door. Jumps up from the couch and runs to KAHLIL)

BROOKES
(Body blocks JUNE from getting to KAHLIL)

Somebody better tell me what is going on right now.

JUNE
KAHLIL is the one who brought me the blanket, he's the one who brought me home. How did you think I got home?

BROOKES
So this is the guy you're cheating on me with?

JUNE
I'm not cheating on you, I've told you a million times I didn't cheat on you and I wouldn't cheat on you.

KAHLIL
Dude, why do you treat her so shitty? You weren't like this in college, what happened to you?

BROOKES
Shut up, man.

You have not treated me right since the beginning of this relationship. And I don't know why I'm just now seeing that but... we're done.

BROOKES

JUNE, you and I both know you're not gonna leave.

JUNE

I know I've tried to leave before but this time I'm serious. It's over. Let's go, KAHLIL.

BROOKES

You're just going to walk away? After this long, you are going to walk away?

JUNE

I never felt safe around you. Every day was a toss-up whether or not you would be happy or angry. Do you know what that does to a person? It makes them think they are the reason you're angry but never the reason you're happy. You scare me BROOKES.

BROOKES

(Ignoring what she just said)

You know, I always knew you were a slut but I didn't realize it was this bad.

(Turns towards KAHLIL)

And KAHLIL,really? We were good, we were friends, why go behind my back and be with my girl?

KAHLIL

Dude, slut shaming, really? I didn't think you were that low.

JUNE

I'm not "your girl."

(Angrily)

I was never "your girl."

KAHLIL

And by the way, I never got with her. We're friends. That's what friends are for. When you drive by your friend sitting on the side of the road, you pull over. You talk to them. And when you find out their boyfriend is the reason they are like this, you help them.

BROOKES

You know what?

(Puts both his hands up and then lightly claps them together)

Fine. Leave. I'm better off without either of you.

(Sits back down)

JUNE

(Runs to KAHLIL and begins walking down the hallway)

BROOKES

(Walks to the door and reaches for the doorknob)

JUNE
(Begins sobbing while hugging KAHLIL)

KAHLIL
(Hugs back)

END PLAY

Made in the USA
Columbia, SC
24 May 2022

60798613R00157